Y0-BRV-943

The World's Classics

CCLIV

THE THREE DERVISHES
AND OTHER PERSIAN
TALES AND LEGENDS

OXFORD UNIVERSITY
PRESS
LONDON : AMEN HOUSE, E.C. 4
EDINBURGH GLASGOW LEIPZIG
COPENHAGEN NEW YORK TORONTO
MELBOURNE CAPETOWN BOMBAY
CALCUTTA MADRAS SHANGHAI
HUMPHREY MILFORD
PUBLISHER TO THE
UNIVERSITY

THE THREE DERVISHES
AND OTHER PERSIAN TALES AND LEGENDS

FOR THE MOST PART TRANSLATED
FROM HITHERTO UNPUBLISHED
BODLEIAN MSS.

BY REUBEN LEVY, M.A.

LECTURER IN PERSIAN IN THE
UNIVERSITY OF OXFORD

The World's Classics

OXFORD UNIVERSITY PRESS
LONDON : HUMPHREY MILFORD

These newly translated stories from the Persian were first published in 'The World's Classics' in 1923 and reprinted in 1928.

PRINTED IN ENGLAND AT THE UNIVERSITY PRESS OXFORD
BY JOHN JOHNSON PRINTER TO THE UNIVERSITY

INTRODUCTION

THE question was once debated in an Eastern mess-room why it was, that when a scrap of conversation between ordinary stay-at-home Orientals was overheard, it generally had reference to money. The conclusion reached was that the Oriental—like mankind generally—prefers best to discuss those things in life which he most often desires. Tales of treasure, gained easily by accident or stratagem, therefore form a great part of the repertory of the Persian story-teller. The pictures which he paints for his audience are not those of the opportunities and the freedom which wealth can bestow, but of the actual, concrete, and visible delights of tanks full of gold coin, rich carpets, great palaces, and so forth. With love it is the same. The mainspring of many stories is love, but the hero generally sets out in search of the heroine because he has heard that she is endowed with all the attributes of physical beauty—and there may be more than one heroine to the story.

The various examples that follow of the Persian story-tellers' art are of a kind made familiar by the

' Arabian Nights '. Few of them have that skilful tying, and subsequent unravelling, of a ' knot ', which characterizes a good novel. They are rather romances, in which the hero, after passing through many dangers by the way, at last reaches his goal, and lives happily ever after. It has been pointed out that the element of poetic justice is often lacking in these stories. But when love or treasure is the motive, it is not to the Persian narrator's purpose to be in the least degree edifying. He gains his applause by lavish descriptions of the beauty of his princess—descriptions all familiar to his audience, for they are of a regular stereotyped pattern—or by using his imagination to the utmost to picture great masses of precious stones and metal—which must be easily negotiable— discovered in appropriate surroundings. When his purpose is to edify, he sets about his task in due form, so that his story becomes a religious homily.

The Story of Zuhak is an exception to the other stories in this collection. It is taken from the *Shah-nama*, the ' Epic of Kings ', a *corpus* of Iranian legend composed in verse by the poet Firdawsi, in the eleventh century of our era, for Mahmud of Ghazna. This monarch, who was amongst the greatest of the conquerors of India, rewarded the poet very shabbily for his work ; and the story goes that Firdawsi, being in a public bath when the Emperor's messenger arrived, handed over the gift which he brought to a passing vendor of beer.

The ' Generosity of Hatim Tai ' is one of a number of tales describing the adventures of that Arabian hero, who is the pattern of the generous man, and whose noble qualities have been made the subject of innumerable stories. The remaining tales in the volume are newly, and for the first time, translated from various manuscripts in the Bodleian Library. The majority are taken from collections of short tales of varied authorship, collected by different hands and brought to England by such travellers and officials as Sir William Ouseley and his brother, Sir Gore Ouseley, the ambassador to Persia. Occasionally, however, the stories have been included in some other work of more serious content. That entitled ' The Treasure of Mansur ', for example, was inscribed in the margins of a valuable work on Mongol history.

The ' Story of Khurshidshah and the Princess of China ' is an incident taken from an enormous twelfth-century novel—the earliest Persian work of the kind—which contains, in three large quarto volumes, an account of the innumerable adventures of one Samak the Brigand. With that exception the tales are all of a length which a story-teller could narrate at a sitting, though in the originals they are somewhat longer than in the translations, which omit tedious repetitions and other portions that are suited more to the taste of the *diwan-khana* of an Oriental prince than to an Occidental drawing-room.

Like nearly all Persian literature, the tales owe their origin to wandering litterateurs who invented characters and incidents to provide amusement for some patron, and who doubtless were rewarded according to the amount of entertainment they had given. The fact, however, that certain themes occur in numerous recensions shows they have grown from some piece of folk-lore, current for generations in Persia. Just as the epic in verse arose from the hero-legends of ancient Iran, so romances had their origin in legends which can be traced, some to traditions of Arab knighthood, others to Jewish or Muslim sources, and yet others to imitations of famous love-stories, such as that of Joseph and Zulaykha. The supernatural world too is laid under contribution, both in its higher aspect of divine intervention, and the lower one of peris and divs, fairies and demons, and of wizards and witches.

The free and familiar employment of the extra-mundane as an element in what often pretends to be plain narrative of fact should occasion no surprise. The people for whom these stories were meant had an acquaintance with the topographical details of Paradise and Gehinnom; and blessings, curses, and the evil eye all had a real, substantive existence for them. Moreover, according to them, the stars in their courses might fight with you or against you. Against this background it is possible to see how the narrator of such tales as these, probably telling them in a dimly-lit chamber after the setting of the sun, worked upon the emotions of his audience. If they do not have the same effect to-day, the stories are at least interesting as illustrating one side of the Persian taste in prose.

R. L.

CONTENTS

	PAGE
THE THREE DERVISHES	1
THE STORY OF THE FIRST DERVISH . .	2
THE STORY OF THE SECOND DERVISH . .	6
THE STORY OF THE THIRD DERVISH . .	11
THE STORY OF ASHRAF KHAN . . .	19
THE STORY OF SALIM THE JEWELLER OF WÁSIT	33
THE GENEROSITY OF HATIM TAI . .	55
JAMSHID AND ZUHAK	68
THE STORY OF THE SAILOR AND THE PEARL MERCHANT . . .	80
THE TREASURE OF MANSUR . . .	92
THE PALACE OF NINE PAVILIONS . .	102

Introducing the stories of

AKHTAR THE CUT-PURSE . . .	112
AFZAL THE SOOTHSAYER . . .	120
NAHID AND HER HARP . . .	126
KHURSHID AND THE WHITE GENIE .	132
NASIR, THE BUTCHER . . .	140

PAGE

The Qazi 150

The Enchanted Island 156

Sayyara, the Son of the King of the Greeks 164

The Prince of Kashmir and the Holy Sheikh 170

KHURSHIDSHAH AND THE PRINCESS OF CHINA 175

THE THREE DERVISHES

It is related that in time past, in the kingdom of Khurasan, there lived a monarch, just and perfect, generous and pure of soul. Men called him Ashraf the Just. It was his custom to ride upon horseback every three days round the bazaars and streets of his capital, with a few attendants, in order to ascertain if his officers truly presented before him all cases of hardship suffered by his less fortunate subjects. Therefore he often visited the poorer quarters, to learn for himself the circumstances of the poor and needy.

One day, as he took his ride, he observed, in a corner of the money-changers' bazaar, three dervishes sitting in a group; and overheard each reciting a verse. The first declaimed:

Once more to gaze upon my love do I desire,
The hope to see again doth many men inspire.

The second dervish continued:

What thou dost, do by thyself,
Whether good or ill it be;
None can do to please thy soul
What thine own hand doth for thee.

The third recited:

Whoever doeth good, doth into Tigris throw it,
And in the wastes again doth God on him bestow it.

Ashraf, on hearing this, thought to himself that the dervishes must be men of learning and understanding who had seen the world; and he desired

B

to converse with them, in order to discover
their true history. Therefore, calling one of his
attendants, he commanded him to summon the
three dervishes to his court; while he himself
returned to the palace. The attendant approached
the dervishes and said : 'Ye pious dervishes, and
ye that sit in conclave, ye whose countenance is
an adornment, the king hath summoned you;
arise, and let us go to him.' In much perturbation
they asked why the king required them, and debated on the reasons for it, until the servitor told
them it would be discourtesy to hesitate longer.
Whereupon they rose and went to the king's court,
and paid due honour to him as they entered.

The king welcomed them honourably, and
ordered food and drink to be brought. Then,
when they were seated, he told them that he had
seen them at the roadside and had overheard their
recital of verses, of each of which he desired to
know the occasion. He added that when they had
concluded their narrative he would himself relate
a history. The first dervish thereupon began as
follows :

THE STORY OF THE FIRST DERVISH

Your Majesty, you must know that I am of
the town of Nishapur, the son of Master Sa'id the
jeweller, and I am called Hafiz Jalil. In my youth,
Heaven endowed me with a handsome countenance
and a sweet voice, which delighted all that heard
it. Whenever I went out of doors a thousand
persons would gather round, standing in amazement at my beauty; until finally, from the impor-
tunities of my admirers, my father no more allowed

me to leave the house. But he was at last persuaded to let me remain upon the roof and delight men by my singing. One night, as I sang, I beheld in the sky a white bird which alighted on the roof. It was of the form of a falcon, but of the size of a camel, and upon it were inscribed many figures and signs. While I sang, the bird cried, shook its head, and remained in ecstasy. Every night it came, and when I had finished singing, it flew away and disappeared. One night I thought to myself that I would capture the bird and keep it prisoner. I pretended therefore to act as usual, but suddenly I leapt forward and seized it by both feet. The bird, however, sprang off the roof, and flew with me high into the air.

When day broke I looked below me, and beheld a scene as though the universe were covered with water, in the midst of which the world floated like a flat cake of bread in a pond. I feared greatly at the sight, and prayed to Heaven to incline the bird down from the zenith and to set me down in my own country. When I had finished my prayer, the bird swooped downwards, and when I looked again, I beheld a deserted spot in which was a garden, and in the midst of it a palace. The bird flew towards this and, as it approached, I unloosed my grip and cast myself on to the roof. For a time I lay there stunned and senseless. Then I arose, thanking God for my deliverance, and descended into the palace. I beheld a chamber of unsurpassable beauty, in which stood a throne of red gold covered with trappings of like magnificence. In front of it was spread a great feast, with jewel-studded goblets and vessels of plucked tulips. But no one sat at the feast. For some little while

I wandered in the palace, and though within it I saw apartments full of gold and jewels, and outside were kitchens and store-chambers filled with food and drink, yet I saw not a single person.

Opposite the door of the palace was a raised couch, and a lofty portico, in which was a fountain full of water. In the midst of this was sunk a column, and crouching upon it was the figure of a lion. From its ears and eyes water poured forth into the fountain. The water was clear as liquid crystal, and for a time I remained there, washing my hands and face. Then I walked about the garden, beholding flowers and fruits of every kind, but all fresh and luscious. Some of this fruit I ate, then again returned to the fountain, where I sat wondering whither the people of the house had departed. I waited until evening, and then I beheld a flock of pigeons which alighted on the roof, and there rested. One by one the birds flew down, drank a little water, and then flew into the palace. I imagined that their nests were there; when, after a little while, to my amazement, I heard the sounds of music and singing from within the palace. As I sat listening, I beheld a peri emerging from it, whose like for beauty I had never seen. She called out to me that the queen desired to see me, and I approached; thinking how beautiful the queen must be, if this was but a subject.

How can I describe the bewitching beauty of the company which I beheld on entering? I was marvelling which of them could be the queen, when a voice fell upon my ear saying: ‘Why do you stand amazed, Hafiz? Turn and speak with me.’ I turned: aloft on the throne was a bewitching maiden, the delight of whose form filled me with love for her, so that the bird of my soul flew out from the cage of my body. She again invited me to approach and speak with her, and for long I conversed, and recited to her many exquisite poems. This I continued until dawn; then, one by one the company disappeared from the chamber. Thinking that they had gone out to the fountain, I approached it, but no one was in sight, and all day I roamed, filled with longing, through the palace and gardens; but the object of my search was nowhere to be found.

As night fell, however, I again beheld the flock of pigeons upon the roof, and, as before, they flew into the palace, from which there soon issued the sound of music and song. On hearing this I entered, and was greeted by the sight which I had before beheld. Long I sang and sighed to her upon the throne, but she permitted no approach, and as day broke she again disappeared.

For many days this continued; until at last, made desperate by my love, I stepped upon the throne and kissed her hand. Thereupon, crying out at my presumption, she dealt me a blow which flung me senseless from the throne, and I found myself once more upon the roof of my father's house, whither my father's servants gathered at my cry. Since then I have never again beheld the peri, and that is why I repeat:

Once more to gaze upon my love do I desire,
The hope to see again doth many men inspire.

The king was pleased at this tale of marvels, and turned to the second dervish for his story. He began:

THE STORY OF THE SECOND DERVISH

O king, while water and earth remain, do thou prolong thy rule! Be it known to you that I am an inhabitant of Balkh, and my name is Khalil. My father was a merchant of great wealth, whose treasures were numberless, but he had no son but me. Many arts and sciences I learnt, and since I was handsome of form and figure, my father loved me greatly.

When I arrived at the age of fifteen years, my father designed to take me with him upon a journey, so that I might learn the art of buying and selling. We therefore prepared our caravan and set out for China, where we arrived in a city at an appointed time. There we alighted at a caravanserai, and busied ourselves with buying and selling.

One morning, when I had been awake for some time and had prepared myself for prayer, I found that my father had not yet risen. I called out to him therefore to ask whether he still slept or was awake. He replied that he was awake, but that such weakness had overcome him that he could not rise. I at once summoned a physician, whose treatment however was of no avail, for a few days later my father died, having warned me to return home to my mother and sisters. After an appropriate time of mourning I set out for my native land with a caravan destined for Turkistan.

We had been one month on the way from China, when a band of robbers fell upon us, stole all that we had, and slew all who were with the caravan. Me too they wounded and left for dead; but when they departed I was able to rise, and, with tottering steps, naked and hungry, I turned my face again towards China.

When, after many days' journeying, I arrived in the town where my father's tomb lay, as soon as possible I made my way to it and poured forth my woes there. As I lay weeping, I fell asleep, and in a dream I beheld my father, who asked me why I had not obeyed his dying behest and returned home. I was about to reply when a hand touched my face, and I opened my eyes. I beheld an old man, a Turanian, dressed in a white robe and seated upon a camel. In attendance on him was a slave, who held the piece of wood in the camel's nose wherewith it is led. I greeted the old man, and he replied to my greeting, and asked whose tomb that was whereon I lay. I told him it was my father's, and at his invitation told him my history, with many tears. At sight of my weeping, he bade me not to grieve, but to rise and accompany him. Accordingly I arose, took his stirrup, and was helped by him into the saddle. We rode on until we came to the old man's abode. There I beheld a house of great splendour, and knew then that he was a rich merchant. When we entered, he bade me be seated, and ordered food and wine to be set before me. He told me further not to grieve. 'Henceforth', said he, 'I will be your father. I have riches and property in abundance; and it shall all be thine.' He commanded rich and luxurious garments to be brought to me, which I donned after bathing. When I emerged from the house, I beheld a fine horse waiting for me; and thus in every respect I was treated as if I were the old man's son.

For two months I lived at ease, until one day as

I lay upon a couch reciting, the master having departed upon a short errand, some one quietly entered, and I felt myself held in a passionate embrace. To my amazement, I saw that it was the young wife of the master of the house. When I asked what she did, she cried out that she had loved me deeply from the moment that I had come into the house, that she had a poison wherewith to slay her husband, and that afterwards she and I could live happily together. In horror I repelled the thought, reminding her what treachery and base ingratitude it would be to slay the man whose salt I had eaten. Again she pleaded with me, and at last, when I refused to agree to her plan, she exclaimed in fury that I should regret it. I fled from the house in horror, while she went into another chamber and arranged with her step-daughter that as soon as the old man arrived, the girl was to appear, torn and dishevelled. The wife would then explain that I had attacked the maiden, and also that in the struggle which followed, I had injured them both. The old man would then slay me in anger.

It fell out as she had arranged. When the merchant returned home, he beheld his wife and daughter bleeding, and with their clothes rent, and he was naturally enraged against me. He sent a message to a brick-kiln which he owned near the city, telling his workmen there to throw into the kiln the first person who came; his intention being to dispatch me there on a pretended errand, and so have me consumed in the furnace.

When I returned home, knowing nothing of this plot, the old man asked me to go to the kiln and see that his workmen made greater haste with their task, for he had need of bricks. I went as I was bid; but it happened that before the brick-kiln was reached there was a fine garden, belonging to a youth with whom I had some acquaintance. As I passed the gate, I heard the sounds of music; and my friend, seeing me on the way, invited me to enter and join in the merriment. I intended but to enter and see what there was, and then to continue my errand; but I was so agreeably entertained that I remained for some time.

Meantime, the wife, either in triumph or remorse, put on her veil and came hastily to the brick-kiln to see what had occurred. In accordance with the instructions which had been given them, the workmen seized her, and threw her into the kiln, where she was consumed.

Now, when the master heard that his wife had gone out, telling no one whither she went, he understood that the matter concerned me, and at once came with all haste to the brick-kiln. But he was too late. When he arrived, his servants told him that his wife had come there, and that, as he had bid them, they had seized and burnt her in the kiln. In a dazed manner he returned home and I met him on the way. On approaching, I told him what had occurred and why I had gone into my friend's garden, and asked his forgiveness. He, however, gave me no reply. I asked him, therefore, why he was so distraught, and the only answer he made to this was: 'God is in Heaven'. At this I suspected the matter of his wife, and told him what had occurred. He laughed at my story and said: 'My wife did not tell it thus; she had a different history.' I begged him to call his daughter and the slave-girls who were in the house to give their testimony. Before entering the house he bade me remain behind, and I therefore halted at the door when he entered.

The old man then summoned his daughter and bade her tell him truly what had occurred. She replied: 'I have never seen this youth, but I know that from the day he came my mother's behaviour changed. She sighed and wept constantly when he sang. Then, to-day, when you had left the house, she clad herself in costly garments and entered the chamber where the youth was. In a little while she came forth with a tooth broken and tore my dress, telling me to say nothing at all when she told her story except: "It is true". Also she threatened, that if I did differently she would not leave me alive. I agreed therefore; and soon afterwards you entered. I do not know what you said to her, but she came back soon, weeping. Like one distracted she donned her veil and left the house, I know not whither; nor has she yet returned.'

When the maiden had completed her story, the old man came to me and begged forgiveness of me for his suspicion concerning me. Then he took me into the house, and, sending for a qazi, he betrothed his daughter to me. A few days after the wedding the old man told me what had occurred to his wife, and how she had been consumed in the fire. He concluded: 'My son, he that does evil will be overtaken by his own evil.'

My wife bore me several sons, and, when her father died, we lived happily for some time on his riches. Then my wife died; and in my grief at separation from her I became a qalandar, and wandered abroad in the wilds, where these two other dervishes became my companions.

I have now therefore explained why I recite
the verse :

> What thou dost, do by thyself,
> Whether good or ill it be ;
> None can do to please thy soul
> What thine own hand doth for thee.

The king was much pleased with this narration,
and turned to the third dervish for his story. He
began :

THE STORY OF THE THIRD DERVISH

Your Majesty, I am the son of Alamshah,
ruler of Merv Shahjahan, and my name is Afzal.
I was reared in great splendour, and grew to be
a handsome youth. When I was fifteen years old,
my father began to seek a bride for me, and everywhere made inquiries for a maiden suited to my
station and talents. One day news came that
a caravan had arrived from Qandahar. My father
thereupon sent for the caravan-leader, and asked
him whether the king of Qandahar had a daughter.
He replied : ' I have heard that the king of Qandahar has a daughter of surpassing beauty. She
was once betrothed to the prince of Turkistan,
but he died the morning after his betrothal. I saw
his coffin as it was on the way back to Turkistan.
She has been betrothed numerous times since then,
but each time her betrothed has died after holding
converse with her.'

I was filled with wonder at this story, and set
my heart upon seeing the maiden. Day by day
my desire grew, but since I knew that my father
would forbid me to ask her hand in marriage,

I decided at last that I would go without his knowledge. One night, therefore, I took gold and jewels from his treasury and set out on horseback for Qandahar. For ten days I travelled, until at last I reached a green meadow, where I dismounted and let my horse graze. I myself shot a bird, and sat down on the side of a pool to cook and eat it. As I washed the flesh in the pool, a great number of fishes collected and eagerly nibbled at it. I perceived that they were very hungry, and so I cut up the meat into small pieces and threw it into the water. While doing so, I observed one big fish which came quite close to the edge. I plunged in my arm and brought him out of the water on to the bank, where he struggled in agony. Being thereon seized with pity for him, I threw him back into the water ; then made my meal, and fell asleep. In a few moments I was aroused by a touch on my face, and I awoke to see a handsome old man, lithe and active in appearance, standing before me, with his cloak tied at the waist, a bow over his arm and a bundle of arrows at his side. He carried a sword, and on his feet were well-fitting shoes. In the wallet which was open at his waist, I perceived several cakes of bread, and two roasted fowls. These he cut up, sprinkled salt over them, and began his meal, calling out to me : ' Welcome, young man, let us dine first and then ask each other's history.' We therefore set to and ate until we were satisfied ; and then the man asked me who I was, and whence I came, and upon what errand I was going. I told him all, and he in return told me that he was a wanderer in the desert, and that he had left his abode in order to see what he could find to take back with him to his wife and children.

His name, he told me, was Awazu'l Hayat, which being interpreted means ' The Substitute for Life '. I asked him whether he travelled in pursuit of some skilled occupation, or whether he came on a hunting expedition. He replied : ' I am skilled in every craft in the world, and all trades prosper in my hand.' Thereupon I asked him to join with me in our travels. He answered that he would do so willingly ; but on one consideration, namely, that we were to share equally everything that came into our hands. I agreed, and he desired me to write him a document to that effect. I told him that I had neither pen, nor paper, nor ink, and at once he produced them and put them into my hand. In the document I wrote as follows : ' Let God, the Prophet, and the angels be aware that everything which comes into our hands shall be divided into two portions.' Then I sealed it and handed it to him.

Putting the document in his bosom, Awazu'l Hayat went away and brought me my horse, which I mounted. He remarked that the object of our search lay a long journey in front of us, and that the greater the speed we made the better it would be for us. When I mounted, he walked by my side. After a little way I invited him to take my horse, but he replied that he was accustomed to travelling afoot, and bade me drive my horse faster. But though I lashed my horse to its greatest speed I could not overtake the man, who remained running in front.

After several days' march, we arrived at Qandahar, alighted at a caravanserai, and took a chamber in it. I gave my companion some money wherewith to buy carpets, utensils, and arms. Then he looked to my horse, doing to it all that was necessary after the long journey. On the fourth day after our arrival, we presented ourselves at the king's court, and paid our compliments to him. The nobles and courtiers after due ceremony led us before him, and he treated us with great good-will, seating us in a place of honour and having food and wine set before us. Then he asked whence we came, and the object and purpose of our coming. Awazu'l Hayat replied that I was the son of such and such a prince, that I had presented myself in order to do service to the king. Further, in answer to a question from the king, he said : ' This prince has heard that you have a daughter. Now his father has heard the history of this maiden and does not approve of the prince's coming. But he, without his father's knowledge, has presented himself before you to ask your daughter's hand in marriage, and he is here in the hope that you will not turn him away disappointed.' The king replied that there could be no question of his giving his daughter, and he greatly pitied the youth that wooed her. ' Would to heaven she died,' he cried out, ' and so saved these innocent youths from destruction.' At this Awazu'l Hayat said : ' Perhaps by treatment from me, that sickness which afflicts her may be repelled.' ' Tell me what this sickness is, if you know it,' was the reply, ' and when my daughter is cured, I will give her to the prince.' ' That is not easy to do at once,' said Awazu'l Hayat. ' First I must see the maiden, and the prince must hold converse with her. Until then it is not possible to treat her.'

The king, however, remained unyielding, until his nobles and courtiers persuaded him to let the treatment be undertaken. Then he consented, and ordered preparations to be made for the wedding. Awazu'l Hayat, however, said that he must act with circumspection, that I and the maiden must be left alone together, but that he himself would be in the chamber with us, concealed from our sight. He continued : ' If after their converse the prince is still alive, then preparations for the wedding may be set afoot ; otherwise, what need for preparations ? ' The nobles of the state approved this, and the king sent for a qazi, who was to betroth the maiden to me.

We remained in the king's presence until night. Then a chamber was prepared for me near the king's own dwelling, and there Awazu'l Hayat said to me, ' If you wish to achieve your desire, you must not fail in any particular to obey what I enjoin.' I promised to do all he commanded, and he continued, ' To-morrow you must request that a spacious hall be prepared for you, with a throne, upon which the maiden must be seated. When you enter the hall, remain before the couch until the attendants and others have left it ; then ascend the throne and seat yourself by the maiden's side. Rise again immediately, however, descend from the throne, and walk towards the doorway without glancing behind you, that I may see what occurs.' I replied, ' I will do it, but tell me what the object of this is.' To this he only answered : ' I beheld a vision, in which it was told me that you must act so, if you wish to attain your desire.'

My chamber was a spacious apartment, nearly fifty cubits long and twenty broad. In the midst of it a throne had been placed, and when day dawned, the maiden seated herself upon it. I was amazed at her beauty, and wondered what it was in her that brought death. I remembered the instructions of Awazu'l Hayat, and went up to the throne. When I approached, the maiden attempted to rise, but could not. I ascended the throne, seated myself by her side, and bade her not to disturb herself. She, in her turn, made room for me, and held out her hand, which I however refrained from taking.

As I seated myself, I beheld that the maiden was agitated in strange fashion. At once I leapt from the throne and ran. She cried out to ask whither I was going, but I gave no reply, nor did I glance behind, but ran directly to the doorway. I had scarcely reached it, when I heard the sound of a sword cutting and slashing, and also the voice of the maiden exclaiming aloud. When I looked behind, I beheld Awazu'l Hayat holding a blood-stained sword in his hand, and a serpent about ten cubits long which he was hacking into pieces. I swooned at the sight, and fell senseless to the ground in terror. But in a little while Awazu'l Hayat raised my head and restored me with medicaments, saying : 'Have no fear and arise, your object is achieved.' When I arose I saw that the maiden had fallen senseless upon the throne. I ran to her and placed her head upon my bosom, while Awazu'l Hayat opened the doors and called the servitors. The king too entered, and remained astounded at the sight which met his gaze. Turning to my companion he asked : 'Whence came this serpent ?' and Awazu'l Hayat replied, 'It was around the waist of the princess, and through fear of it, she could tell no one of its existence.' 'But how did you know of it ?' asked the king.

'I have a familiar jinn,' was the reply, 'and he informed me of it.'

Then they poured oil of violets and of almonds and vinegar into the nostrils of the maiden, until she recovered. When the king questioned her, she said : 'Seven years ago, while I was asleep in the garden, a serpent came and twined itself round my body. Whenever I wished to tell any one of it, or to disrobe, the serpent threatened to attack me, and whenever a man seated himself by me it struck him and killed him. Out of fear of this jinn I could say nothing.'

All present were astonished at this history, and the king gave orders to beat the drum which announced good tidings. Then with royal pomp our wedding was celebrated. For six months longer we remained at Qandahar, after which we set out for my own country. Awazu'l Hayat accompanied us until we reached the halting-place where I had made his acquaintance. There he bade the servants pitch a tent so that the fountain lay in the midst of it. When all our company were settled and at ease, I asked Awazu'l Hayat when we were to depart from thence. He replied that he would there separate from us, and go to his own home. I asked what had occurred to make him decide upon separation from us, and pleaded with him to come with us, giving him a promise that I would fulfil his every desire. He replied that he had a longing for his household and his family, and he could no more remain away from them. 'If you have a favour to bestow, it is well ; but if not, then I must depart.' I said : 'So be it. As you know, all that I possess belongs half to me and half to you.' I then took paper and pen and divided all my belongings into two equal portions, inviting Awazu'l Hayat to take whichever he desired. But he turned to me and said: 'You share all your belongings, but you do not share the most essential part of all.' I thought again of all my possessions, but nothing further occurred to me. At last I asked him what he meant, and he said: 'The princess.' 'But,' I said, 'how can we divide her? Will she live?' 'That,' he said, 'does not concern me.' 'Take all I have,' I begged him, 'but leave me my wife.' But he refused, and when I begged him to take the princess himself, he refused that also. Then he departed, and I remained in the tent in the greatest despair. When I went out I saw that he had bidden the escort to withdraw to some little distance, that none of them was to approach the tent, and that no one else was to be permitted to approach it. Soon he returned with four pegs and a rope, and when I asked him what he was going to do with them, he said that he intended to divide the girl into two halves, one half to be his and the other mine. At this I wished to leave the tent, but he held me fast, threw me to the ground and bound me securely, hand and foot. In spite of the girl's cries and mine, no one approached the tent. Then he bound the princess to the four pegs in the ground and drew his sword. Turning to me, he said, 'Do you desire the upper half or the lower half?' Our cries were terrible to hear, but he took no heed, and waved his sword over the maiden, until, in her terror, she burst into deep perspiration. At once Awazu'l Hayat turned to me and said: 'My purpose in all this was to free this lady from all the poisons with which the serpent had imbued her. Now you may live happily with her always.'

I begged him to take all our wealth, but he replied :
' You must now be made aware that I am that fish
which once you took out of the water, and which
from pity you threw back again. I found life again
then : your life and that of the princess are now
substitute for my life. When you threw me back
again, I prayed Heaven to give me the form of
a man, that I might gain your wish for you.'
Having said this, he leapt into the water and
became a fish again.

My wife and I at last, with great regret, turned
our faces again towards my native land, where my
father welcomed us with joy. When, after the
lapse of years he died, I became king. But then
my wife died too, and I, having appointed in my
place the son who had been born to me, set myself,
in sorrow at her loss, to wander over the earth. It
chanced that I met these other two dervishes on
the way, and since then I have accompanied them.

Now you know why I exclaim :

Whoever doeth good, doth into Tigris throw it,
And in the wastes again doth God on him bestow it.

Ashraf was delighted with this history, and then,
turning to the dervishes, he said : ' O dervishes,
your stories are good, but I too have a history and
an adventure to tell.' They begged him to relate
it, and he began :

THE STORY OF ASHRAF KHAN

My father was king of this country. When I
was seven years old, he set me to schooling, and
appointed a teacher for me. Until I was twelve
years old I was engaged every day in writing and

copying, and became acquainted with the sciences. In beauty also I excelled, and I determined to become expert in the exercises of the field, in riding, archery, and the arts of chivalry. For six years more therefore I devoted myself to these pursuits, until I attained so high a degree of boldness and power, that there was none who could force open my clenched fist or bend my bow; and my father greatly approved my strength and vigour.

One night as I lay asleep, I saw myself in a dream, mounted upon a white horse ascending towards the sun. Soon I arrived at a garden raised on high, beautifully green and fresh. I entered it without dismounting, and saw in the midst of it a palace of white marble, so carefully built that the space between stone and stone was not visible. Still upon my horse, I entered the palace. On one side of the hall was a throne of sculptured marble, and upon it were soft pillows, upon which lay a maiden of surpassing beauty.

When I saw the maiden in my dream, I almost cried out for joy. Not with one heart, but with a hundred, I fell in love with her sun-like beauty. I desired to dismount from my horse and go to her, but found that I could not. Then her glance fell upon me, and she said: ' O prince, it is indeed wonderful that you remember me.' I replied, ' I wish to come and pay my regards to you, but I cannot.' She said to this: ' Asleep at ease upon your pillow, how can you come grieving to me ? ' The joy of gazing upon her woke me from my sleep, and I could not forget the thought of her face. I marvelled to myself at the wonderful vision I had beheld, and pondered long what I could do. Then

another night I found myself again in converse
with the maiden, who said to me : ' O Ashraf Khan,
have you forgotten me ? I cannot be your bride
until you come and free me from these heavy
bonds with which I am fettered. Arise, come to me.
Think nought of distance or of the perils of the
road, or of the trials of heat and cold ; for I keep
the eye of expectation upon the road, and it is for
your sake that I suffer the woe of these bonds.'

Again I leapt from my sleep, and I was like to be
demented with love of the maiden. I could not
restrain myself. There and then, in the middle of
the night, I made my preparations, mounted my
horse, and left the palace, making my way towards
the sunrise, without warning either to my father or
my servants. I took no count of road or no road,
but the whole of that day I let my horse carry me
forward and also the whole of that night. It was
only when prayer-time came next morning that
I dismounted, and allowed my horse to graze
a little. Then I mounted again and rode farther.
So for twenty days I travelled night and day, not
knowing whither I went. At last I reached
mountains, whose height was beyond compute.
There I continued my way, beholding marvels
innumerable. One day my horse fell dead upon the
mountain-side, and I was forced to continue my
journey on foot. I tied my skirts as a girdle about
my middle and walked on. Two or three days
later I shot a wild goat, roasted its meat, ate it, and
then again I continued on a way full of many
marvels and wonders.

At length, after a long space of time, I reached
a city whose towers and ramparts were exceedingly
high, and whose inhabitants were tall of stature

and terrible. They seized me and spoke to me, but I understood not a word of what they said, nor did they understand me. At length they brought me to a building which looked like a school, but on the four sides were four raised couches, while another couch stood in the middle. At one side hung a wondrous curtain of cloth of gold, so richly embroidered that the stuff of it could not be seen. All the people in the building also were clad in jewel-encrusted garments. They placed me before the curtain of cloth of gold, and from behind it I heard the sound of hissing breath, as though of a bull slain for sacrifice. I gazed about me, wondering whether this was the place in which my object was to be attained, or whether it was to be the place of my destruction. In a little while the hissing ceased and I heard a voice, very terrible. At sound of it, all that were present prostrated themselves, and I too bowed my head in obeisance, but in my heart I prostrated myself to God.

When I raised my head again, I heard a sorrowful voice from behind the curtain which said : ' O Ashraf Khan, you are welcome.' I replied : ' Your Majesty, may your lofty shadow remain for ever over the heads of your servants.' Again I bowed down. Then the voice said : ' You beheld in a dream the beauty of Shamsa Banu, daughter of Kaywan Shah, and became enamoured of her ? ' I answered, ' Yes, and my hope is that I shall not be turned from this noble court ashamed, and with my object unattained. What may I do to achieve it, and by what road may I reach it ? ' The voice replied : ' It is not for me to lead you there, but I will give you a sign of where it is. Go out of the

door and go towards the sun, turning towards the
right hand. It is a journey of six months' duration.
You will reach mountains of the range which you
have already crossed ; go farther towards the sun,
and you will find what you seek.' I asked : ' Is
it indeed so, that I shall behold the object of my
desire, and see again that maiden ? ' The voice
answered : ' You will see her, and it is decreed that
you will be joined to her.'

On hearing these words I was filled with joy,
and said : ' If your Majesty permit, I will depart.'
But the voice said, ' Remain with me as my
guest for three days,' and I replied, ' It is for
your Majesty to decide.' Then the voice uttered
words which I did not understand. Several persons
came, took me by the hand, and led me to a
chamber, marvellously adorned, where I remained
at ease for three days. On the fourth day
I was again led to that other building. There
I made obeisance, and the voice said : ' Behold,
Ashraf Khan, you are about to depart. You will
see many marvels and wondrous things, and will
suffer much toil and hardship before you reach the
object of your desire.' I said : ' I will make the
thought of you my guide on the way, and your
regard and favour towards me will satisfy me.'
The voice then again bade me go. Once more
I bowed to the ground and rose again.

Then jewels were put in my hand, and I was led
out of the door, where indication of the road was
given to me. So I departed. On my way I beheld
many marvels and wondrous creatures, amongst
whom I walked in amazement. Some of these
fled from me, others attacked me so that I was
forced to slay them. At last I reached the shore

of a stretch of water, a mighty river, upon the banks of which I saw a number of creatures lying dead. Some had no backs, but had two bellies and eight feet like those of asses, and their heads too resembled asses' heads. They had tails like camels', and while their bellies were white, the rest of their bodies was black in colour.

A little way farther on I came to an island, upon which were several strange monsters of men, whose form I can scarcely describe. Each was one-half of a man, having one arm and one leg ; and from the crown of the head to the foot, they had but half a man's body, one eye and one eyebrow, one hand and one foot. But they hopped faster on one foot than I could run with both of mine, so that I could not overtake them. In fine, I beheld so many wonders that they are beyond me to describe.

When I had crossed the river and left it behind, I came to another mountain range, which occupied two days in the ascent. On the night after I reached the top, I beheld myself, in a dream, arriving at the abode of the maiden whom I sought. She greeted me smilingly and called me to her, saying that God had made her my bride. My great joy at beholding her awoke me from sleep, and I continued my way full of the thought of her beauty. After descending from the mountain range, I crossed a level desert plain, where sometimes for three or four days together I found no water. After struggling onwards, suffering a thousand tortures, I reached a city, large and far-spreading. I entered the gates and saw shops on all sides. The people gazed at me, but none addressed me, so that when at last in the bazaar

I came upon a cook-shop, I determined to hold some converse with the owner. I therefore halted in front of the shop and greeted him. He replied in exceedingly friendly fashion, led me into the shop, and prayed me to be seated. You would have said that he had known me and been my friend for thirty years. Then he brought me delicious food to eat, and asked how I did. I told him my history, whereupon he said : ' This place is the entrance to the mountain of Qaf. I have no knowledge of that city of which you speak, but on three sides of this mountain there is a city, and on the fourth is a sea which none of us can cross, but it lies between my country and yours. Now that it has fallen out that you, whether through love or chance, have arrived at this city, will you leave immediately or will you remain here for some days ? ' I decided that I would remain and throw off care ; afterwards I would depart. I told the cook therefore that I would remain in the city, whereat he said : ' If you desire to depart, I will make every preparation necessary for your journey ; if you remain, it is customary in this city for no man to remain lonely. There are three women's hammams here, one of which belongs to the chief of the women. Do not go there or they will slay you. The other belongs to the widows, and the third to the unmarried maidens. Go and seat yourself at the door of either of these, and when the women pass, pluck the robe of any one that pleases you, but speak no word.'

Following this direction I seated myself at the door of a hammam, where I saw women arriving in crowds. All turned their faces towards me and

then entered the hammam. I thought to myself
that there might be others more beautiful than
these, and so waited. Soon a woman appeared,
young and beautiful beyond compare, with whom
were many slaves and attendants. As she approached and looked towards me I plucked her
robe. At once she turned towards me, saying with
a smile : ' Remain here until I leave the hammam.'
Then she entered, but soon emerged again, and
bade me not to move from where I was, so that she
might not lose me. She said further that she would
send some one to bring me. In a little while I saw
a couple of slaves approaching, one carrying a case,
and the other leading a mule with a saddle and
trappings. They greeted me and bade me welcome, and I arose and accompanied them to
a hammam. When I emerged, they took from the
case a complete and valuable set of garments, in
which they clothed me. Then I mounted the mule,
and, with the slaves leading, we proceeded to a
splendid house, of which the inside was elaborately,
nay, wonderfully, adorned and decorated, and
upon which great pains had been spent. There
was in it a dais covered with flowers like a garden
in spring, whereon I seated myself. To one side
was another chamber, and issuing from it I heard
the voice of my enchantress, welcoming me. After
some converse with me she sent for the qazi, who
soon came, and when I had paid my respects to him
he betrothed us. In return he was given a robe of
honour and a purse of gold, and he departed, while
we remained to delight in our pleasure and joy.

The next day, as I left the hammam, a slave
appeared and presented a document before the
dame. When she had read it, she turned to me

and said, ' My husband was the king's vizier until
he died. Now it is the custom in this city, that when
any one of the king's servitors dies, his post is not
given to another until his widow has married again.
If the new husband desires the office of the old, the
king appoints him to it; if not, it is given to
another. This letter has come from the king,
asking if you desire to be his vizier.' I thought to
myself that if I accepted the office I should be tied,
and I saw no means of extricating myself. Moreover, I had no need of the king's viziership. I
answered my wife accordingly, and she approved.

Some days later, as I sat in converse with her at
the side of a fountain by our couch, I felt myself
suddenly overcome with heat and perspiration,
and said : ' How hot the weather is ! I am burning.' No sooner had I said this when my wife,
opening her hand, struck me a heavy blow on the
face. Then she rose, and, covering her face from
me, called out to her slaves : ' Drive this un-
believer away from my sight.' As they seized me,
I asked what the reason was for this, and she said :
' You have become an infidel and deserve death.'
' But why ?' I asked; whereupon she replied : ' You
pass judgement on God, in whose hand is every
decision, who regulates the world as He desires.
What concern is it of yours if the air be cold or
hot ? ' Then she said to her slaves : ' Go to the
qazi and bring a decision.' At once they departed,
and brought back judgement that I was to be
slain. No heed was paid to my cries, and the
king's slaves drove me out along the road to my
fate. As we passed by the shop of the cook,
I called out to him : ' In God's name, friend,
save me from this calamity.' He approached and

asked what had occurred. I told him, and he replied : ' Yes, you have become an infidel to our faith, and they will slay you.' I begged him to rescue me, telling him that if he did so I would leave the city. Thereupon he went to the qazi and told him that I was a foreigner, and that I had acted in ignorance. Also he presented himself before the king, asking for a decree to expel me from the town. Immediately he had obtained it he returned, took me from the hand of the king's slaves, and accompanied me to the gates of the city, through which he cast me out, telling the gate-keeper not to admit me again. To me he said that if I returned I should be slain. I replied : ' If I return, let them slay me.'

Then I turned my face towards the sun, and came after many days' travel to a mountain, whereon were creatures with bodies of elephants, though larger. From some I was forced to flee, but others paid no heed to my existence. Beyond them I came to a desert, of which you would have said that its veins ran fire. When I placed my foot upon it, the very marrow of my skull was scorched. For three days I walked, hungering and thirsting, until I was powerless to continue. Falling to the ground I made obeisance to Heaven, and with tears I said : ' Alas, it were pity to die in this waste, without meeting my desire ! ' When I raised my head I beheld a peri, clad in green, from whose face flashed fire. When I had filled my eyes with his beauty, I felt strength return to me, and I greeted him. He returned my greeting and asked : ' What do you desire from God ? ' And I replied : ' My desire is to reach the abode of Shamsa Banu, daughter of Kaywan Shah.' He said : ' Give me your hand, place your foot behind mine, and cover your eyes.' I did so. Then he said : 'Open your eyes,' and, when I obeyed, I beheld a meadow and a greensward, fresh and luxuriant, and in the midst of it a pleasant fountain.

Then, giving me a loaf of bread, the peri disappeared, while I went to the water's brink and sat down. There I ate my bread and felt new strength come to me, and discovered myself filled with boundless delight. For a little while afterwards I wandered in the meadow, and beheld, at some distance, a fortification. As I neared it, I saw a green and delightful garden, which was filled with fruits of all kinds and with flowers of every colour. It was such that the garden of Paradise might envy it. In the midst stood a lofty palace. It was covered inside with felts and carpets, and its walls were of marble, which reflected like a mirror.

Leaving the palace again, I saw a couch in the garden, and upon it lay a wondrously beautiful maid. Her hair was fastened to chains, and she was bound hand and foot. When I beheld her I was like to fall with astonishment, but when that sweet-lipped beauty cast her gaze upon me, she bade me welcome, and said : 'For long I have beheld you in my dreams, and the good tidings of your coming have been with me. I was told that such a youth as you would come to release me from these heavy bonds of mine. I was bidden to tell you that I have lived for seven years in these bonds. Also I was made aware that Ashraf Khan, a youth of high rank and great power, would be my deliverer, and further that I should become his bride. For three years now I have waited for you.'

When I heard her words, I was filled with joy. First I loosened her face and hair, and then I loosened all her bonds. For long we remained in converse, mingling together like milk and sugar. Then suddenly I heard a voice cry out: ' O thou, born of man, who are you ? What are you that come and take from my hand my beloved, the object of my desire, this maiden, beautiful as the moon, with the countenance of a flower ? I have come to fill your skull with earth.' I looked round to behold a male div, hideously ugly and of most malignant appearance, whose body was like a mountain, and whose head like a great dome. His arms were like two great branches of the chinar tree ; his mouth resembled a cave, while his eyes were like two dishes filled with blood. Every tooth was the size of an anvil, and two horns grew out of his head, like those of an ox, but far larger. He wore a garment of leopard's skin, and wound several times round his middle was a great chain. Upon his shoulder was a mighty wooden club shod with iron and stone. As he approached, the maiden fled in terror into the palace ; but I leapt up nimbly, drew my sword and stood firm. Suddenly I saw that he had swung his club at me, but I leapt to one side, raised my death-dealing sword, and plunged it into him, with the name of God loud upon my lips. He fell to the ground and called out: ' O thou man-born, thou hast slain the div to whom all the divs of the mountain of Qaf paid obedience, and whom they all feared.' Seeing him utterly helpless, I bade him tell me how I must go on and what way I must take. He said : ' You cannot take the road by which you came. On two sides of this palace are desert, mountain and plain.

On the other two sides is the sea. You cannot go either by sea or land.' However, when I heard him speak of the sea, I thought to myself that that would be a possible and a better way.

I then entered the palace and found the maiden, who was trembling in fear of the div. I reassured her, telling her that I had slain the monster, whereupon she rejoiced greatly, and she was still further comforted, when she went into the garden, to see him lying dead upon the ground. Then we filled a sack with jewels, and, leaving the palace and the garden, went on our way towards the sea. On arriving on the shore we found a great number of trees growing there. I took the branches of these, plaited them together and made a great raft. Upon this we seated ourselves and, having commended our souls to God, we launched ourselves upon the face of the waters.

After a long period of voyaging we reached an island, where I beheld three ships lying upon the beach. As soon as we touched the land we made our way to the first ship, which we found full of treasures and stores. Human bones also lay about in it, which I buried. Then, gathering fruit, both dried and fresh, of which the island contained great quantities, I provisioned the ship. This, however, was fast in the mud, and it required the labour of several days to dig a channel with sufficient water to float the vessel. When this was done I hoisted sail, and with an oar I set the ship in motion.

We remained in that ship for eight months, wandering upon the waters, until at last, by God's favour, we reached an inhabited inland. When the inhabitants of it asked who we were, and whence we came, I told them that we were sailing

from Hind to Frang when a storm came and
wrecked two of our ships. We were like to drown,
but by the grace of Heaven we had come to that
island.

We remained there until five other ships were
ready to accompany us. Then I bought slaves and
goods of all kinds and we set sail, with a great
company of people and much wealth. After
making favourable progress, one fortunate day
we landed on our own coast, and I made my way
immediately towards Khurasan. Before I arrived,
I sent a messenger forward to my father, who sent
out his nobles and chief officers to meet me. A
great feast was prepared, and with magnificent
ceremony I was wedded to the maiden.

When in due course my father died, the nobles
and officers of the state brought me out of my
mourning, and, placing a jewelled crown on my
head, seated me upon the throne of sovereignty
in my father's stead. Since then my wife has borne
me two sons, and we live happily together.

When Ashraf Khan had completed his history,
the dervishes prayed for the long endurance of his
kingship, and marvelled at the strangeness of the
story. Then the king treated them with great
favour, and sent one with them who should accompany each of them to his own city or friends. This
story has remained in remembrance of them, but
Allah best knows the truth.[1]

[1] [MS. Ouseley 389, fol. 1 ff.]

THE STORY OF SALIM THE JEWELLER OF WASIT [WÁ-SIT]

THE historians relate, that by the time that the tyrant Hajjaj became ruler of Wasit, he had slain most of the scholars and philosophers of Iraq, and had wrought cruelty upon all the innocent inhabitants of that land, so that all men feared his name. One day, as he sat in an ill mood upon his throne, Hajjaj drew his sword and placed it before him; then, calling a servant, he told him immediately to bring his chamberlain Fattah. When Fattah, trembling with fear, presented himself and asked his desire, Hajjaj said to him : 'I desire you to find a story-teller who can relate an adventure of his own that will make me both laugh and cry; and so distract my thoughts. I wish you to bring him now.' To this Fattah replied, 'I obey, my lord, but where can I find such a man at once ? Grant me but little delay that I may search.' Hajjaj thereupon agreed to allow him three days; and, heavy of heart, Fattah returned home.

Full of care and fear, the chamberlain thought to himself, 'Where can I find such a man ? If I search over the whole earth, there can be no man of experience so varied. I may as well put on beggar's robes at once and flee from this monster, for he will surely destroy me if I do not find the man.' All the chamberlain's friends were amazed at the tyrant's command, and cast about for a man such as was required. But they could bring no one to mind.

Now Fattah had a young daughter, whom he loved dearly. She approached him as he sat deep in thought, and asked what ailed him. He told her what was required of him, and at once the girl departed. Early next morning she returned and said : ' There is in your dungeons a man who has had just such an adventure as Hajjaj requires. His name is Salim, and he was once a jeweller of Wasit. Go down and call him, for if you search the whole world from east to west you will find no man to equal him.'

In great joy Fattah ran down to the dungeon, opened the door, and called out : ' Is there any man here whose name is Salim ? ' and from the depths came the answer: 'Such am I.' Fattah opened the dungeon door wide and told the man to approach. Slowly there emerged from the dungeon an old, white-bearded man, with a bandage over his face, his nails long and his hair matted. On his feet were chains, and round his neck an iron collar. Great age had bowed his body and shrivelled his skin, and his eyes were unseeing. So feeble was he that words came from him only with difficulty. Fattah looked upon him in amazement, and asked : ' Master, how long have you been in that dungeon ? ' He replied : ' It is twenty years since I last saw the light of the sun, or heard my name called, or since any one remembered me. I do not know what has happened, or what angel told you concerning me.' Fattah replied : ' You have lived long in woe. I wish to know whether you can relate your history, so that Hajjaj may both cry and laugh at it.' The old man replied : ' I alone could relate such a history, and when Hajjaj hears of my adventures, he will both laugh and cry.'

They bathed the old man with hot waters, and anointed him with oil until his veins were softened. He was given a suit of clean garments, and a great bowl of white sugar was set before him, that he might eat of it as much as he desired. They fed him on lamb, and chicken, and butter; until his strength returned, and his eyes brightened, and his body straightened out in renewed strength.

Then Fattah took him, and led him before Hajjaj, and said: 'This is the man whom you desired to tell you his adventures.' Hajjaj asked where he had found him, and the chamberlain replied that his daughter had told him there was such a man in the dungeon. 'How did your daughter know that?' asked Hajjaj. 'She is but fourteen years of age, and you say that this man has been in prison for more than twenty years. Bring your daughter that I may question her.' Fattah thereupon brought his daughter, and asked her how she knew of the existence of the old man. She replied: 'May your Majesty live long! My mother used to tell me that on the night when I was born she was lying on a couch under a tree in her garden. Suddenly a woman appeared before her, beautiful as all the fairies, and she took me in her arms and praised me and welcomed me. And she said to my mother: " Just as you bore a child under this tree, so have I borne one here, but my child is a son. Know therefore that I am one of the Mussulman fairies, and I wish the two children to be brother and sister. I desire you to suckle my son, and I will suckle your daughter and will thus bestow upon her this advantage, that if ever misfortune befall her, she has but to come under this tree and pluck a branch from it. Then if she place that upon a fire, my son will at once appear to give her aid." I had never yet seen my foster-brother; therefore, when I saw my father in trouble at your behest, I went into the garden, plucked a small twig from the tree which my mother had pointed out, and put it upon the fire. At once a youth appeared, who asked me what my need was. I told him that you desired my father to find such and such a man, and that my father was greatly at a loss to know what to do. He replied: "There is only one man in the whole world who can relate an adventure such as will cause Hajjaj both to laugh and to cry, and his name is Salim, the jeweller of Wasit, who is lying at present in the dungeon of Hajjaj."'

Hajjaj was amazed at this story, and, giving the girl ten pieces of jewellery and other presents, he dismissed her. He then turned to the old man and asked for his story, telling him that if he succeeded in entertaining him he would reward him and set him free, but that if he failed, he would leave him in his dungeon until he died. The prisoner then thanked him and began as follows:

My name is Salim, son of Abdullah the jeweller of Wasit. My father lived in this town, possessed of great wealth, both in money and lands, in cattle and slaves. On the day when I was born, he gave away two thousand dinars to beggars, and entirely clothed twenty orphans. Also he invited all the inhabitants of Wasit to a feast, the like of which had never been seen in the city. When I was old enough to be taught, I was set to learn the Quran until I knew it by heart. Then he engaged a learned tutor for me, and I read sixty Arab books, and was taught etiquette and languages. The art of rhetoric, and of letters, and other accomplishments also, were taught to me, until there was none in Wasit to equal me. Other tutors he brought, who perfected my knowledge of geometry, philosophy, interpretation of the Quran, astrology, and the like. I also read the history of the Arabs and Persians. Moreover my father engaged a tutor to teach me the arts which are of use in an assembly, such as chess and singing. Also he brought horsemen and champions of single combat to teach me how to ride, wield a sword, and draw a bow; and how to engage in battle, both mounted and afoot. So capable did I feel myself at last, that I could have attacked a mountain single-handed and overcome it.

My father was greatly pleased at my progress; and matters continued thus until, in my seventeenth year, my father laid his head on the pillow of death. But before he died, he called me and told me that he bequeathed to me all his wealth. Also he gave me four pieces of advice: not to cast good fortune to the winds; not to suffer tomorrow's grief till to-morrow; not openly to point out a fault in another, nor to tear off the cloak in which God Himself has clothed His servants, that is, to be content with all that comes, both good and ill, for God has ordained all; and lastly, never to be ashamed of any labour, for he that is ashamed of a task is put to shame by all. That very day— may your Majesty live a thousand years—my father died.

I mourned for the customary period, and for long went without pleasure or even comfort. Then my inheritance came into my hands. Steadily I spent it, sitting long at wine with those that flattered me, and ate up my wealth with those whom I held to be my friends. I bought all that I desired and gave away far more, until I had consumed all my father's wealth. For though you fill a house with gold coins, yet if one of them be spent each day, the time will come when the house will be empty.

Then to my wife, who was my cousin, I said: ' Arise and go to your father's house, for you have been accustomed to luxury and ease; you cannot remain in this discomfort. I, however, will stay in this land until Allah sends me either fortune or death.' My wife replied to this indignantly: ' Guard thyself against feeble-mindedness! Do not despise work, for it was given by God. It is woman's place to stay at home, and man's to go abroad and work. Why should I go to my father's house and leave you seated in idleness here ? ' I told her that I had no trade other than the selling of jewellery. My father had followed that trade too, and he amassed a great fortune, for he knew the value of jewels, bought cheaply and sold dearly. I, however, had now no capital, and that trade therefore was closed to me. She replied: ' Do those that do not sell jewellery die of hunger ? There are a thousand trades in the world by which men earn money, and there are many which need no capital and yet produce money. Your enemies rejoice sufficiently over your downfall. Take an axe and a rope, go out to the mountains and cut wood ; or bring thorn-bushes from the desert; or else make bricks or weave carpets, sweep floors or sieve corn ; there is no work that brings disgrace. Put your hand to one of these tasks and let us eat bread. I will help by washing clothes, or by any

other work that women can do. But I will not go
to my father's house. I ate your wealth when you
possessed it, and now that you have nothing I will
be content.'

Her words put new strength into me, and
I thanked God for so loyal a wife. I decided to
become a porter, thinking to myself that mastery
in this profession depended on strength and that
I was powerful of body. I sold my soft garments
and bought a coarsely woven one, which I donned.
With a rope over my shoulder and a girdle of palm-
fibres I went out and sat down among the other
porters in the bazaar of Wasit. My enemies jeered
at me, but I paid no heed to them and engaged in
my trade. Two hundred, three hundred, and even
five hundred maunds were an easy load for me, and
what the other porters carried for a dirham
I undertook for half. There was not a day upon
which I did not bring home ten dirhams to my
wife, who praised and encouraged me. I became
so well known that people who had loads would
employ none but me, and would wait ten days in
the expectation of having me.

At last the other porters were inflamed by Iblis
with jealousy of me, and they banded together to
slay me. Some amongst them were cunning, and
said : ' The slaying of a man is beset with difficulties, and the spilling of blood is like garlic. Let
us invite him to be our chief. We will pay him
ten dirhams a day; that will keep him at home
and he will not enter into competition with us.'
This they did, and for a year I lived thus in ease.

Then one day, in the stormy season, I went into
the bazaar. It had been raining, and mud lay deep
everywhere. As I passed through the market-place

I saw a man with a heavy load, whose foot sank deep into the mire, so that his load fell off. Twenty men gathered round him and endeavoured to lift the bale, but no one succeeded. In pity therefore I cast off my clothes and went to his aid. When I had lifted the load out of the mud and carried it out of the bazaar, all that stood by applauded, and I then went to a pool near by to wash myself and put on my clothes. Hardly had I put my foot into the pool, when I heard a cry from behind: 'Salim, thou didst a manly act, yet didst not thank God for thy strength, nor give praise to his Prophet.' I turned at these words and beheld an old man with a white beard and green eyes, who stood glaring at me. Trembling fell upon me at sight of him, and I could scarcely ascend from the pool. By the aid of a youth who was with me, I made my way home, and fell grievously sick.

After a little while this came to the knowledge of the porters, through the youth that brought my daily salary. This accursed fellow persuaded his companions that I would never more be able to carry on my work as a porter, and advised them to cease their payments to me. They followed this advice, and I was soon compelled to sell in three months all that I had gathered together in two years. When at last I had paid for my medicines and my special foods, nothing was left me. I was now even poorer than before, for my strength had departed. I reproached myself bitterly for having relied upon my youth and strength rather than on the help of Heaven. I vowed therefore, that if I were cured and my health restored, I would henceforth devote myself to the service of Heaven. That night I beheld a glorious vision, in which the

Prophet, beauteous to behold, appeared to me and held out his hand to me, saying : ' Wilt thou keep thy vow always ? ' I replied, ' I will keep it.' The vision vanished, and when I awoke in the morning no trace of my sickness or weakness remained. My arm was stronger than it had ever been, and I perceived a power within myself which I had never before felt.

When I left the house, I had not a coin in the world. I decided to leave Wasit and go to Kufah. There I met a caravan of pilgrims going to Mecca. I helped them in the feeding and loading of their camels, and was well rewarded for my trouble ; then I accompanied the caravan to Mecca. Having performed the rites of the pilgrimage, I made my way to Medinah, where I visited the tomb of the Prophet, upon whom be peace. Thence I made my way by turn to Halab, to Lantaqiya, and finally to Tarsus. This was a wealthy city, where I remained for a year in attendance on the mosque, earning my living by serving the warriors of the guard. It happened one day that they were to make a raid on a town in Rum, Amudiya by name, and I was permitted to join the army. For nine days we marched, and on the tenth we beheld a wide plain, in the middle of which was a fortress guarded by a mighty army. I was told that they numbered ten armies of unbelievers, in each of which was ten thousand men, and that each man had sworn not to return until the dust of Tarsus was thrown into the sea. We Mussulmans numbered only twelve thousand, and I thought to myself that it was hopeless to think of victory.

Now it was the custom of these Rumis to send out a champion, who would stand forth alone in

order to challenge the enemy. On the morning
appointed for battle, there rode out from amongst
them a knight who was the nephew of Heraclius,
the Rumi captain. He was fully clad in armour,
and held in his hand a spear which dragged on the
ground. He came towards us, and with boasts
asked us to provide some one to oppose him. No
man of us stepped forward however, and for long
I hesitated; until, at last, roused by his taunts,
I decided to give him battle. My friends attempted
to dissuade me, but I told them that I had
not come to look on; but to slay or be slain.
Taking my reins in my hands, I galloped out and
curvetted in front of the army, speaking praises to
God.

The Kafir champion shouted towards me, but
since I did not understand a word of what he said,
I shouted back ' *Wasit, Wasit*,' meaning that I was
a man of Wasit. It was the custom to call out the
name and lineage of every champion. I occupied
myself little with this form, but instead roused
myself and came upon him like the wind. In
a moment I plunged my spear into his breast,
threw him from his horse, and slew him. Neither
the army, nor the Kafirs, nor even I myself, believed
this possible, but the cries of the enemy told me it
was true. They sent a message to their captain,
Heraclius, informing him of what had occurred:
' The champion of the raiders', said they, ' is
known to none. He neither manœuvres nor
circles, but gallops from a corner and thrusts with
his spear. Moreover he makes no reply to aught
that is said to him except " *Wasit, Wasit!* "'

Heraclius was filled with rage and grief at what
he heard. ' This man must be either a mighty

champion,' said he, ' or a great fool, who does not
know what he has done, or whom he has slain.
I will give to any man that avenges the death of
my sister's son and brings me this man's head,
a hundred thousand dinars, a hundred sets of
garments of Rumi brocade, a hundred slaves and
a hundred slave-girls, a hundred Arab horses, and
also any city that he may choose from the whole
of Rum.'

There was then brought to Heraclius a man
named Sham, who said he was ready to venture
his life in order to gain the reward that was offered.
They clad him in armour from head to foot, so that
nothing of him was visible save his eyes.   His
Arab steed had pointed ears, eyes black as crows,
a broad chest, and legs like columns for strength.
It pranced and curvetted as it was being saddled,
but it was firmly held, and over its head was placed
a coat of armour.

As I stood between the ranks of the two armies,
I prayed for aid and victory, while Sham came
towards me. As he approached, I charged upon him
and thrust my divinely-directed spear straight at
him, so that it made no account of armour, but
thrust him through. His horse, when its rider was
flung to the ground, galloped in amongst the ranks
of the Mussulmans, where it was cut into pieces.

I was determined to stand forth until victory
was achieved for us, but I was dissuaded from
fighting again that day, and so rested until the
morrow. At earliest dawn I arose, donned my
armour, and rode forth in front of our ranks.
One after another there came forth twenty
champions from the ranks of the enemy, and in
turn I slew them all, so that the Mussulman army

shouted with joy, while the unbelievers were dispirited. The next morning, the enemy sent a messenger to beg for peace; but we demanded a hundred ass-loads of silver for every man in their ranks, whereupon he returned greatly discouraged. That night the enemy took counsel together and said: 'If we make peace, our treasuries will all be empty; if we fight, the Mussulmans will conquer by reason of the courage of this Wasiti. We must defeat him by a stratagem. A pit must to-night be digged in front of the ranks of the Mussulmans and covered over, so that when he rides out in the morning, he will fall into the pit and be slain.' To this all agreed, and the pit was digged.

Contrary to their usual custom, the enemy next morning shouted and rejoiced, so that we imagined they had gained reinforcements. Full of fury at this, I galloped out and shouted my challenge. Several men of them stood forth a little way and hurled abuse at me, and towards them I galloped in great anger. They turned in great fright and I followed, not knowing what was in store for me. Suddenly I felt myself plunged into a pit, and, weighted down with a hundred maunds of armour, I could do naught. The men that had stood forward immediately ran to the pit and made me a prisoner. They bound my hands, drew me out of the pit, and carried me, with a hundred thousand slights, before their king. With great joy he commanded me to be securely chained hand and foot and placed in a dungeon, where there were already three hundred Muslim prisoners. Further, he said that he had sworn a vow that he would make peace with the Mussulmans as soon as I was captured.

For some time I remained in the prison. Then, one day, aided by the drunkenness of a prison guard, I made my escape. For four days I wandered, eating fruits from trees on the way, and on the fourth day I came to a river, which I crossed by means of a raft made from the branches of trees woven together. When I had crossed, I wandered for a whole day until I came to a great tree, which I climbed. From it that night I beheld the marvels of the river. One of these was a cow, that emerged from the water and produced from its mouth a jewel which illumined the night. This it laid on the bank, where it shone, so that I was seized with a desire to know whence its brightness came. When day approached, the cow took the jewel and sank again into the river with it.

I decided to remain where I was for that day, in order to see what would occur that night. When darkness fell, the cow again emerged out of the water, but this time with a jewel a thousand times brighter than the one I had seen. This it laid on the bank, so that I became very impatient to behold it near by. Very cautiously I descended from the tree and approached the jewel. Then, taking up some clay from the bank, I threw it over the shining stone, so that it was at once hidden. I then climbed back into the tree and waited to see what would happen. When the light disappeared, the cow uttered an evil bellow, and after galloping wildly about for a little while, it plunged into the water. Again I climbed down from the tree, took up the jewel, and made my way onwards.

Thus I travelled for some time without incident, until I came to a great troop of apes. The farther I walked in order to escape them, the more numerous they became. When night fell I concealed myself in a tree trunk, so that I might observe them in the morning. Suddenly, as I sat quietly watching, to my great horror they came towards me. But they did me no hurt, and I observed that their houses were made of sticks plastered with mud. Their trees were covered with many fruits, which they cooked and ate. In great troops the apes approached me, and I, in endeavouring to escape from them, went on to the roof of one of the houses and sat there. But they brought me down and took me into the house, where I beheld an enormous female ape, whom they treated with great deference and to whom they brought constant supplies of nuts and dates.

They set me down before her and pointed to me, and, at a sign from her, nuts and dates were also given to me, and I ate. When night came they brought me soft grasses for mattress and pillow, and she lulled me to sleep by embracing my feet.

When Salim reached this point in his story, Hajjaj burst into laughter and asked what followed. The reply of Salim was filled with the details of his life in the city of the apes, how he remained there for many days and gained the affection of all. He told what food he ate, how long he slept, and what he did daily, until at last sleep overcame Hajjaj and he heard no more.

The next day, Hajjaj summoned Salim and bade him continue his story. He thereupon proceeded as follows :

May the prince live long ! I remained for some time with the apes, but at last in weariness

I escaped from them and again went on my way. After three days of travelling I came to a forest in which were many wells. About these were numerous trees laden with fruit and many dwellings, good to look upon. Seated at the door of one of them I beheld a man who bade me sit down with him. When I had sat a little while, he asked me whether I was not hungry and whether I did not desire some food other than fruit, upon which I must have for so long existed. I replied that I would gladly eat something other than fruit, and he bade me enter the house. I had no sooner turned my back upon him to do his bidding than he leaped upon my shoulders from behind and clutched my throat with both hands. I was like to die, but at last he released his hold though he still clung to my shoulders. Still gripping me he led me out of the house and made me gallop up and down, and whether he ate or moved or slept he kept me in this torment for many days, with his legs clutching my neck and with his heels in my ears. If I was slow or forgetful, he dug his teeth into my head until I shrieked aloud to Heaven with the pain thereof. One day, as I walked in the wood, I beheld many vines laden with grapes. The thought came to me to ferment some of the juice, which would help me to forget my woes. I obtained vats, therefore, which I filled with grape juice, leaving it in the sun to ferment. Then I drank it and became light-hearted and red of face. The leather-legged throttler, on beholding this, also begged some to drink. For long I refused it, but at last gave him a large quantity, which he drank eagerly. Very soon he became deeply intoxicated, shouting and plunging about on my shoulders. The other throttlers, who gathered together at his cries, laughed aloud at his antics, and asked him what had occurred to affect him thus. He told them that out of grapes I had prepared for him a drink, which was the most delicious in the world. They, too, asked for some of it, and soon they were all overcome. Observing this, I unloosed the legs of my tormentor, dashed him to the ground, and made off as fast as my wounds would permit me.

As I went, I applied healing leaves to my body, and assured myself that the jewel, which I had sewn into my garments, was still safe. For six days I walked, hungry and thirsty; until at last, in the midst of a desert, I beheld a great tree, and, underneath it, a pool. As fast as my feebleness would allow me I took off my clothes, washed away the last traces of the vile throttler, and then fell asleep. As I awoke the next morning, I beheld, sitting in the branches of the tree, three white pigeons. While I gazed, filled with the thought of my hunger, they beat their wings, and were transformed into three beautiful maidens, a hundred thousand times more beautiful than the moon, and wonderfully clad. After conversing together for a few moments, they played and swam about in the pool, leaving their garments on the side where I lay concealed.

Now while they were intent upon their play, I crept out and took a cloak that lay near me, that which had been put down by the most beautiful of the three maidens, who seemed to be sisters, and returned stealthily with it to my hiding-place. When they had brought their play to an end and had come out of the pool to dress, the maiden whom I had robbed cried out that her cloak had been taken away. They searched everywhere near them, and seemed filled with astonishment that the garment should have been lost. Suddenly their glances fell upon me, and they exclaimed: 'There is a man, who has been sitting here. He must have the cloak!' She whose cloak I had taken remained behind, while the other two approached, but she called out: 'Welcome, Salim! I have long burned to see you, and now I find you here. Give me my cloak and let me lead you to my father.' I replied: 'Princess, who are you and what is your name, and how did you know my name?' To this she said: 'If you do not know me, I know you well, and what adventures befell you in Wasit and in other places since then.' And she recounted all the various incidents of my wanderings, to my great astonishment. I asked again how it was that I did not know her, and she replied: 'My mother bore me for your sake, and until I came into the world I was called by your name. But now is not the time to relate that history. Give me my cloak, and let me go and inform my father and mother that you are here.'

I then gave her back her property. Then, telling me to take her right hand and to close my eyes, she carried me up into the air. After a moment, she told me to release her hand and to open my eyes, and when I did so I found myself in a green meadow, filled with saffron, hyacinths, and gilly-flowers. In the midst of it flowed a stream of water, whiter than milk, and by it a castle which towered to the zenith. Its pinnacles were of gold, and reached to a great height. At the gate was a shop, at the door of which an old man was sitting, and he was pointed out to me by the maiden as her father. I approached and greeted him, and he rose and led me into the shop with many compliments. 'O Salim,' he said, 'we are well acquainted with the trials and woes which you have suffered. My daughter, whose hand you held, is destined for your wife. Tell me if you desire her or not.' I replied that with all my heart I desired her. There and then he placed her hand in mine, and to my great joy betrothed us.

I was then taken into the castle, and I beheld an apartment like Paradise for beauty. In it four couches were set side by side; upon each being a jewel-encrusted throne. The hall was hung with curtains of silk, and upon the floor were laid carpets of great beauty. Rows of slaves stood with vessels of perfumes, which they poured over me at my approach. My clothes were removed, and in their place I was clad in royal garments and was made to sit upon one of the thrones. Musk and amber and sandalwood were burnt for my pleasure; and all my desires were gratified.

With varying fortune of joy and sorrow, I remained in that land for six years; and then there came upon me a longing to see my native Wasit again, and the kinsfolk and friends whom I had left there. One day, as I sat weeping at the recollection of them, my wife beheld my tears and asked what grieved me. I told her that I was drawn back to Wasit; that I knew not if my kinsfolk still lived or were dead. She bade me not to grieve; 'For', she said, 'if you swear an oath that you will return faithfully, I will entrust you to some one who will take you safely, and without any hardship, to Wasit.' I told her that if I broke my oath she might do to me all that lay in her power to do. Then, warning me to keep the matter from her father, who might lay obstacles in the way of my going, and who might even bring me back, she made preparations for my journey.

The next day she gave me a thousand dinars of gold, for she told me that I might need them. Then I beheld a white bird alighting from the air. It was as large as a horse, and, as it approached, the peri spoke to it and said : ' For my heart's sake I desire you to take this youth to the city of Wasit.' The bird replied, ' Your command is laid upon my soul. I will carry him to Wasit in a night. But you know how it is with me. Tell him, that when he is on my back he must speak no word and have no thought of Heaven, for I acknowledge no allegiance to it. If he disobey, I will cast him to the earth, wherever we may be.' This the maiden repeated to me, and then, immediately before we departed, she gave me a comb, a piece of lead ore, and a bottle of quicksilver. ' If my father discovers your departure,' said she, ' and goes in pursuit of you, throw down behind you this comb. There will then appear a great plain, in which you may lie concealed from all beholders, and so escape. If again you are pursued, throw out behind you this lead ore. There will appear a mighty mountain which will keep you secure. If a third time you are pursued, throw out behind you this bottle of quicksilver. There will appear a great sea, the size of which is beyond description. When you have crossed it no one else will be able to follow, and you will arrive in safety.'

I thanked her and bade her farewell. Then I seated myself upon the bird. With powerful flapping of wings it rose into the air and flew until half the night had gone, when from behind there came suddenly a great clamour and tumult. I looked behind me to see a myriad of lions, wolves, tigers, leopards, and wild beasts of every description, which were following us. They were the army of the peris, which the maiden's father had sent in pursuit of us to bring us back. A great fear seized me at the sight, but, remembering the comb, I threw it down. At once we were concealed from view, and flew on safely.

By the time morning broke the bird was wearied, and it alighted on the top of a mountain to rest. Seeing myself once more on the earth I was filled with joy, and naturally, but without remembering the conditions laid upon me, I exclaimed, ' Praise be to Heaven.' The words were scarcely out of my mouth when the bird threw me to the ground, and flew off into the air and disappeared. Whereupon I swooned with terror.

When I returned to my senses, it was broad day. I rose and walked for a little distance until I came to a spring, where I lay down and slept. After a while I went on and came to a steep path, and, having climbed it, I reached a great plain more pleasant than Paradise, in which four thousand sheep were pasturing, and with them an old man of great stature and terrible appearance.

He called out to me to approach and not to fear, for he wished merely to know my history and, in the relation of it, to share with me the woes of my toilsome journey. I was much reassured by his words, and approached and greeted him. He replied : ' You are welcome here ; be seated.' When I had done so he asked how I had come to that place. I answered: 'Water, chance, and God's predestination have cast me down upon this spot.' He thereupon asked me to be his guest that night, and when I assented he invited me to go with him to his house. As we walked he suddenly uttered a great cry, and without warning the mouth of a cave opened in front of us, into which we entered, with all the sheep following at the old man's heels. The cave was of enormous size and branched off in different directions. Into one portion he drove the sheep; then, taking me by the arm, he led me into another cave where I beheld a number of men, both young and old. As I looked more carefully, I saw that they were all bound with chains. Turning to me the old man said: 'Salim, you have suffered much misery, hardship and woe; but behold!'—and even as he spoke he loosened the chains from one youth, killed him where he lay, and rent him limb from limb. May your Majesty live long! At sight of that horror my senses left me, and I fell as one dead to the ground. When I came to myself, the others in the cave commiserated with me, telling me that I had fallen into the hands of an ogre, whose food was the flesh of human beings. Hope left me and I thought to myself that now all my toil and hardship had been for nought, and that never again was I to see my home and dear ones. In despair I cried out, 'I can bear no more,' and in deepest misery and hopelessness we wept all together.

When Hajjaj heard this, he too wept in sympathy; but Salim continued his story and told how finally they slew the ogre and escaped from the cave. After a long journey he reached Egypt, and from thence he accompanied a caravan going to Wasit. He continued as follows :

It was night when I reached Wasit. For seventeen years I had not seen my house and family. As I approached all was dark. I knocked at the door and I heard my wife's voice cry out, ' Who is it that knocks so late at a widow's door ? ' I told her to open the door, and when she did so, in her great amazement at beholding me, she let fall the lamp which she had in her hand, and it was broken into pieces. Since she had no other in the house, I went into the bazaar and knocked at the shop of a merchant there who sold them. He did not know who I was, nor did he wait to hear my business, but he raised a cry that I was a thief, come at that late hour in order to rob him. From all sides a crowd of men gathered. They beat me with their fists and robbed me of all the money which I carried. Then I was condemned to the dungeon, where I have remained ever since.

Hajjaj was greatly pleased with this story, and asked whether, in proof of it, Salim could produce the jewel that he had taken from the river cow. At once he searched in his garments, and laid before the prince a jewel the like of which had never been seen. All the jewel-sellers in Wasit were summoned, but none could gauge its value. Thereupon Hajjaj gave him a great sum of money, and also, taking off his own cloak, gave it to Salim, whom he released for ever from the dungeon and restored to his family, where he lived in luxury for the remainder of his life.

[MS. Ouseley 231, fol. 113^{b} ff.]

THE GENEROSITY OF
HATIM TAI

A CERTAIN king of Khwarazm had a son possessing many talents. Hearing the praise of the beauty of the princess Husn Banu, he conceived an ardent desire to see her. But first, to prove the truth of what he had heard, he sent a skilled artist to visit her and paint her portrait. The painter accordingly set out for Shahabad, where she lived, and on his arrival, in common with other strangers, he was received with great hospitality. The attendants of the palace, after refreshing him and showing him every mark of attention, led him to take leave of their mistress, for he had not told them his purpose. The princess talked to him kindly and gave him money for the expenses of his journey; but the painter had no desire to go farther, and asked to be taken into her service: 'For', said he, 'I would like to spend the rest of my days in this gracious abode.' Husn Banu thereupon inquired his profession, and he said: 'I am an artist, so skilled that I can draw the moon behind a veil.'

After a short time the princess desired to have her portrait painted, but did not know how to contrive matters, for since he was a stranger to her court, the artist was not permitted to see her face. At last she said: 'Can you not draw my face if it is covered with a veil?' He replied: 'No; a better plan would be for you to look down from your balcony into a vessel of water placed beneath, and that will reflect your likeness.' This was done, and succeeded to perfection. The artist painted two exact portraits, omitting not a mole or line of her face, and, giving one to the princess, he kept the other.

Soon afterwards, on the pretence that he wished to see his family, he asked leave to go, and, with money for his journey, he departed, coming back in no long time to the Prince of Khwarazm with the portrait of Husn Banu.

The prince was delighted with the picture and at once set out, without waiting for money or for any preparations, and even without his father's permission.

After suffering some days' fatigue on the road, he reached Shahabad, where he was received with the customary hospitality. The following morning, when the attendants offered him money for him to continue his journey, he refused it, saying : ' What have I to do with money ? ' At last they came to the princess and told her that there was a man who would neither eat the meal prepared for him nor take money for his journey. On hearing this, Husn Banu sent for him and asked why he did not take what was offered, although he appeared to need it. He replied : ' I have left abundance of gold, and want no treasure. I am the son of the King of Khwarazm. Your portrait has infatuated me, and I long to see your face.'

At these words the princess hung down her head and said : ' To see me is difficult. If you were the west wind itself you could not touch my tresses.' ' Then ', said the Prince, ' I must sacrifice my life on your threshold.' ' That ', replied the princess, ' is easy, but to behold me is hard. But, if you are set on this design, you can yet gain me if you will accomplish a certain task; but if you fail, you may never hear my name again.'

The prince eagerly agreed to this, and the princess said to him, 'There is a person who cries : "What I have once seen, I desire to see again." Bring me news of this person and of where he is, and of what he has seen. When you have done so, I will set you a second task.' The prince asked where this person was to be found, but received the reply that if the princess knew, she would send her own servants to bring him. Before he departed he asked : 'How long will you wait for me?' She replied : 'One year.'

So the prince departed with a heavy heart, not knowing where to go first. After long travel he came to the land of Yaman in Arabia, where, as he lay under a tree bemoaning his hard fate, Hatim Tai (the prince renowned in Arabia for his unparalleled generosity) came to the spot, and seeing the youth's distress asked him what caused it. In reply the prince showed him the portrait of Husn Banu and told him the story attached to it. Hatim Tai took pity on him, and took him to his palace, where he gave him refreshment and promised to help him.

After three days they set out in company to Shahabad, and when they arrived Hatim asked to be admitted to the presence of the princess. At last she consented, and said to him : 'Why do you come?' He replied : 'I have heard much of your beauty, and long to see your face.' 'That is impossible,' said she, 'unless you fulfil the task I set.' She then told him what she had told the prince of Khwarazm, namely, that there was a person who said : 'I have seen and long to see again'; and she wished to know what it was that he saw and desired.

Hatim, having received his errand, took leave of the princess and departed. He knew not, however, where to go, and after a few days came to an uninhabited waste, where not a bird spread wing. Here he saw a doe pursued by a wolf, who was just about to seize her when Hatim called out: 'Hold, savage, do you not see that she is a doe and not a hart?' The wolf stood in amazement, and said to Hatim: 'You must be Hatim to have so much compassion on a doe.' 'How', said he, 'are you acquainted with my name?' 'The name of Hatim', answered the wolf, 'is known to all. No one but he could be so kind to brute creatures as well as to men.'

They then fell into conversation on the object of Hatim's journey, and the wolf told him that in the desert of Huwayda such a person had been seen and heard. From the spot where they were, two roads led away, of which that to the right led to the desert of Huwayda. Hatim thanked him and departed. On his way he met a jackal in a trap and released it. The jackal showed his gratitude for this by offering to accompany him to the desert; but Hatim would not hear of it, for he desired to go alone, and he asked only to be shown the nearest way. The jackal then told him that if he continued he would come to a spot where four roads crossed. It would be best for him to take the one that went straight on, and God would without doubt make his way easy for him. Then Hatim dismissed the jackal, and pursued his journey till he came to the four roads, of which he chose that leading forward, as he had been directed.

He had not, however, travelled far when he beheld a herd of a thousand bears, who were foraging with their king. Immediately, they gave notice of his approach to their sovereign, who ordered him to be seized, but after regarding him kindly he directed that care was to be taken of him and that he was to be carried to the palace. On his return there he summoned Hatim to his presence, and, after permitting him to be seated, inquired his business and if his name was Hatim. To these questions Hatim replied fittingly; whereupon the king said: 'You are welcome; I will give you my daughter in marriage, for I have yet seen no man worthy to be my son-in-law, and it was not fitting that I should give her to a slave.'

On hearing this Hatim buried his face in his cloak. 'Why', asked the king of the bears, 'do you thus keep your head down? Am I not worthy to be your father-in-law?' Hatim replied: 'But you are an animal and I am a man; how can we be allied together?' 'O Hatim,' said the bear, 'in pleasures and desires men and animals are one. But set your heart at ease, for my daughter is exactly like you in outward form.'

The bear then commanded that his daughter be decked out and brought to him. When she arrived, the bear said to Hatim: 'Cast but one glance upon her.' Hatim arose, and going out to meet her was amazed to see a maiden like a full moon in splendour and with a human face. Coming back to the king's court he said: 'Thou art a king, and I a stranger; how can I thus break all laws and marry her?' But the king replied, 'Accept her for any reason that pleases you. Are you not the prince of Yemen?'

Hatim then pondered the matter and thought to himself, 'Into what trouble am I now fallen! I came here with a certain purpose, how can I then consent to delay here?' The bear saw his hesitation, and said: 'If you do not take my daughter, I will bind you and hold you prisoner till the end of the world.' Hatim answered as before, and the bear, turning in rage to his attendants said: 'Take this fellow to the cavern you know of, and keep him there.' Immediately Hatim was seized, and having removed an enormous stone from the mouth of a cave, they thrust him in and again closed up the hole with the stone.

Hatim remained in the cave, hungry, thirsty, and stunned, for two weeks. Then the king sent for the captive and addressed him as follows: 'O Hatim, I bid you accept my daughter.' Hatim remained silent. Fruits were then brought and Hatim ate and drank, and when he was satisfied the beast again said to him: 'I bid you take my daughter.' But Hatim answered as before: 'What relationship can there be between man and beast?' So again he was sent back to the cavern and shut in. There he remained hungering and thirsting for several days, until in his sleep one night he dreamed that an old man came to him and said: 'Why do you delay the matter on which you came, not agreeing to what they desire?' Hatim replied: 'If I agree, will they ever permit me to depart on my own business?' The old man replied: 'That is your only hope of release, otherwise you will remain here and die in this cavern. When you have won the favour of the bear's daughter you will easily receive permission to go.'

Hatim awoke from his dream and kept these

words in his mind when, after two weeks, the king
of the bears again summoned him. When the bear
again put the same proposal before him, Hatim
accepted and was led to the apartment of his bride,
where she sat awaiting them in a room spread with
rich carpets and magnificently adorned, while she
herself sat on a couch of gold and jewels. The king
took Hatim's hand and joined it to that of his
daughter, for that is their custom; and so the
wedding was celebrated.

For three months Hatim remained in bliss. For
the first few days he feasted on delicious fruits,
brought fresh for him every day, but at last he said,
' Fruit does not suffice me, I would eat other food.'
So they brought him meal and sugar and sweet oil,
and brought him china dishes for him to eat
therefrom.

At length, Hatim confided to his wife the errand
on which he had come, and asked her to obtain her
father's permission for him to depart. On Hatim's
promising to return, the king of the bears allowed
him to go, and, ordering an escort of his subjects to
conduct Hatim to the confines of his dominions, sent
him on his way. New difficulties, however, awaited
him. He had travelled a few days only when he
came to a sandy plain, barren and desolate. Yet
he proceeded, hoping to find a way out, and in the
evening he met an old man in a long flowing
garment who gave him food to eat, but he had no
water. He directed him, however, to a pool which
lay at no great distance, and to this Hatim
hastened, and stripped off his clothes in order to
bathe as well as drink. No sooner, however, had
he entered the pool than he beheld a fish rise out
of the water, having half its body from the waist

upwards of a woman's form, of great beauty. She approached Hatim and drew him down below the water to where a wonderful palace was built, and asked him to remain there with her. But Hatim told her of his quest, and reluctantly she dismissed him and put him again on land.

Hatim having washed and dried his clothes, dressed himself and continued his travels. At the end of a few days he came to a high mountain. On climbing it, he saw on the top a circular grove of green trees, in the midst of which was spread a fine carpet laid by a clear rivulet. The breeze was cool and Hatim was tired : lying down he was soon fast asleep. In no long time the owner of the carpet appeared, and to his amazement found a young man asleep on it. But hospitality forbade him to disturb the youth, and he sat there till the youth awoke. Having greeted each other they entered into conversation, and Hatim repeated his astounding history. The stranger at length interrupted the story, and said : ' Then you must be Hatim, for surely no one else would so venture his life in the service of friendship. O generous youth, God is beneficent and will help you in your undertaking. Yet, since no one has returned safe from the desert of Huwayda, and since whoever has so returned has been bewildered in his understanding, keep this device of mine in your ear ; for before you reach the desert of Huwayda you will be surrounded by enchantments, from which do not attempt to release yourself by force or violence. Amongst all the enchantresses one more beautiful than the full moon, but with her face veiled, will approach you and put out her hand. But keep your heart firm, and only then,

when you desire to depart, take her hand. As soon
as you do so, you will be transported to the desert
of Huwayda. But if you neglect to carry out my
advice, you will regret it till your dying breath.'

In this conversation they continued till a slave
brought a tray, when, after having washed their
hands, he brought a dish of milk and rice and two
pitchers of water. Hatim had eaten nothing for
some time, so this food was to him delicious. He
spent the night there, and next morning went on
his way.

After some days' travelling he came to another
small lake, whose banks were covered by shady
trees. As he sat cooling himself, a beauteous
maiden emerged from the water and, coming
straight to him, took him by the hand and plunged
with him rapidly below the surface. For some
time they descended, till at last feeling ground
beneath his feet, he opened his eyes and discovered
himself in the midst of a great garden. There the
maiden relinquished his hand and went away and
left him. He himself, being curious to see where
he was, began to explore, but he had not taken
many steps before thousands of beauteous damsels
appeared on every side, and each tried to attract
Hatim to herself. But Hatim paid attention to
none of them, knowing in his heart that the whole
was enchantment. But he allowed himself to be
led towards a palace which they had built of
gems and pearls, and which was adorned with many
pictures.

On entering he beheld a throne made of emeralds,
diamonds, and rubies, and as he approached, the
damsels, without warning, became pictures upon
the walls. Being near the throne, he thought to

himself : ' Since you have arrived here, at least be
seated.' But as he placed one foot upon the step
there was a sudden crash, and he withdrew his foot
hastily, thinking that he had broken the throne.
He began to look under the throne, but seeing
nothing he ascended and sat down. Immediately
another loud noise followed, and looking around he
saw the damsel of whom the stranger on the hill-
top had told him. She advanced, looking languish-
ingly at him with half-shut eyes, and, clad in gleaming robes of gold, stood before the throne.

Hatim longed to remove the veil that was upon
her face, but remembered again what the stranger
had said, and thought to himself : ' So long as
I do not take her hand I may stay here amid all
this enchantment. I will stay awhile until I have
had my fill of marvels, and then I will depart.'
For three days and nights he sat upon the throne.
When night came, candles were mysteriously lit.
Song and music delighted his ears, the picture-
damsels stepped down from the walls and danced.
Meantime, the nymph that stood before the throne
served him smilingly with delicious meats and
fruits of every kind, which were brought in on
trays. Hatim ate of them, but to his wonder his
appetite was never satisfied.

On the fourth day, this thought occurred to his
mind : ' O Hatim ! if you stay here and look on
for a hundred years you will never have seen your
fill, and meantime the unfortunate prince awaits
you.' So he stretched out his hand to take that
of the bewitching maiden before him. Instantly
another nymph appeared from beneath the throne,
and struck him a blow that dashed him from it.
On recovering himself he beheld neither garden,

throne, nor nymph, but on all sides a wide-stretching desert.

Hatim knew that this must be the desert of Huwayda, and at once set out in search of the person whom he had come to seek. He had not gone far when he heard a voice saying: 'I have seen once and long to see again.' Three times this was repeated, and was followed by a deep silence. Hatim hastened in the direction of the voice, but for seven days and nights no one appeared in sight. On the eighth day, towards evening, he saw an old man sitting upon the ground, and coming up he saluted him. The old man returned his salute and said: 'Whence come you, and what is your business here?' Hatim answered: 'Sir, I have a task to fulfil. Tell me truly what it is that you have seen and that you long to see again.' 'Be seated,' said the old man, 'and I will tell you.' Hatim sat down, and two pitchers of water and two loaves appeared mysteriously before the ancient. One pitcher and a loaf he kept for himself, and the other he gave to Hatim.

They ate and drank, and after resting, Hatim again asked his question. The old man replied as follows: 'One day I was sitting by the side of a pool, when out of the water a nymph appeared, took my hand and carried me down into the depths. When I opened my eyes, a wonderful garden appeared to my sight, and rows of beautiful girls stood on every side and drew me towards a throne which stood there. I ascended it and looked about me. Immediately a maiden more beautiful than the moon appeared and stood before me. At sight of her I lost control of my heart, and I took her by the hand to seat her by me on the throne, when suddenly another woman appeared from beneath the throne and struck me so violent a blow that I fell down and found myself in this desert. From that time I have been frantic and cannot forget that ravishing maiden.' Saying this he heaved a deep sigh and ran off, crying : ' I have seen once and long to see again.'

Hatim ran after him and seized his hand : ' If you saw your beloved once again would you be glad ? ' said he. ' It is impossible,' was the reply. ' Come with me,' said Hatim, ' and I will show you how.' So together they retraced their steps, and Hatim showed him where the pool was in which lived the water nymph. There he left him as the nymph appeared, and made his way back to Shahabad.

On his arrival there, the retainers of Husn Banu remembered him and accompanied him to a cara-vanserai, where Prince Munir Shami, whom he had promised to help, came and threw himself at his feet. Hatim raised and embraced him, and when he had related his adventures they went in company to the palace of the princess, who, addressing Hatim from behind a curtain said to him : ' Tell me, brave youth, what news have you brought ? ' Hatim replied : ' An old man in the desert of Huwayda, having seen a nymph in the enchanted regions, became enamoured of her, and, setting his face to the wilderness, continually calls out : " I have seen once and long to see again." ' Then he related the incidents of his visit to the enchanted realms and of his restoration of the old man to his beloved. Concluding, he said : ' No one will hear that exclamation again, for I have given the old man what he had lost.'

Huzn Banu acknowledged with many encomiums that his story was true. A feast was prepared for Hatim, who sat down to it with Prince Munir Shami. To the latter he said : 'You may now approach the princess with some hope of success,' and then, having eaten and drank, he took his leave.

[From the *Asiatick Miscellany*, Calcutta, 1801.]

JAMSHID AND ZUHAK

In the days when the world was young, there was a king who, from his capital in Iran, ruled the earth for seven hundred years. His name was Jamshid, and he was indeed a mighty monarch, for men and divs and birds and peris all obeyed him. The world grew prosperous under him, for he said : ' I will prevent evildoers from working ill, and will guide all men aright.'

For fifty years he concerned himself with weapons of war, to open the path to glory for the valiant, and made helmets and lances and coats of mail. Then he turned to the making of garments for his people. He prepared stuffs of linen, of wool, of beaver skins and of rich brocade, and taught the people how to weave ; and when the material was ready he showed them how to clean it and make it into garments. This being achieved, he devoted a space of time to seeking out the precious stones, and discovered such treasured things as ruby, yellow amber, silver, and gold. Then he invented perfumes, such as balm, camphor and pure musk, aloes, umber and rosewater. Thereafter he discovered medicine, remedies against every sickness, and the means of preserving health and of curing wounds. Thereby he made the world contented and was himself happy.

Three hundred years passed, and in that time death was unknown. There was neither pain nor sorrow, and the divs were kept in slavery, so that they never troubled men. But as time went on, the king became so powerful that he could see nothing in all the earth save himself, and by his arrogance incurred the anger of the gods.

. . . .

Now there lived at this time in Arabia a king among the desert chieftains and the captain of many armed bands of horsemen. He possessed flocks and herds of goats, camels, and sheep, each a thousand strong, as well as cows and Arab horses. This generous king had a son Zuhak, who was brave, light-hearted, and care-free, and who was constantly engaged in wars against his enemies.

It happened one day that Iblis, the god of the divs, came to the palace disguised as a nobleman, and so pleased the young prince that he turned aside from his brave and noble way in order to follow the wicked div. Iblis rejoiced greatly, and said: ' I know many things which none can learn except from me.' ' Teach me them,' said the young man, ' and do not delay.' ' First,' said Iblis, ' you must swear an oath not to reveal my secrets to any man.' ' I swear,' said Zuhak, ' and I will do everything you tell me.' ' Then,' said Iblis to him, ' why should there be any other man but you, illustrious prince, in the palace ? Of what use is a father when he has a son like you ? Take his throne, for it belongs to you, and if you follow my counsel, you will be a great king on the earth.'

When Zuhak heard this he pondered long, for he loved his father. He said: ' I cannot do it. Tell me something else, for that is not possible.' Iblis replied in fury, ' If you do not carry out my commands and if you break the oath you swore to me, my bonds will remain attached to your neck for ever.' Zuhak submitted, and said: ' How am I to bring this about ? '

' I, Iblis, will prepare the means, and raise you to the sun. You have but to keep silence.'

Now the king had around his palace a garden in which he took great delight, and here, often rising before dawn, he would walk, without even one slave to carry his torch. On the path the div dug a deep pit, covered it with brushwood, and spread earth on the top. Early the following morning, before the sun was up, the Arab king awoke and went out into the cold air of dawn. As he approached the fatal pit his star paled, but he disregarded its warning, and, falling into the chasm, was slain. Thus perished this pious man who had scarce ever spoken a harsh word to his son.

Iblis, his plan accomplished, then approached Zuhak again, and said : ' When you have turned your heart towards me, you may obtain all that you desire. Renew but your oath, and the entire world will be your kingdom ; the wild beasts, the birds, and the fishes will be your subjects.' And with these words he vanished.

Soon afterwards Iblis assumed the guise of a young man of ready speech and agile form, and presented himself to Zuhak, saying that he was an excellent cook. The prince engaged him, and by his royal command delivered to him the keys of his kitchen. Now the design of Iblis was to make the prince abandon his eating of herbs and to persuade him to the eating of meat. He began by preparing yolk of egg for him, which in a short time gave him great vigour of body. Zuhak was pleased and commended his cook, who said, ' To-morrow I will prepare for your Majesty a dish than which nought is more perfect.' And the next day, when the blue dome of heaven was lighted by the red ruby of the sun, he prepared a dish of partridge and of silver pheasant, which the Arab ruler ate; and thus he abandoned his imprudent mind to the power of Iblis, who, on the third day, placed upon the table a mixture of birds and lambs' flesh. On the fourth day, when the meal was brought, the king feasted on the flesh of a young calf seasoned with rose-water, old wine, and pure musk. The meal filled him with delight at the skill of his cook, and, summoning him, he said, 'Think what it is that you desire, and ask it of me.' Iblis replied, 'I have but one request to make of the king (may he live prosperous for ever), but that is an honour too great for me; it is that I may be permitted to kiss his shoulders and to touch them with my eyes and face.'

Zuhak suspected nothing of his intention, and said: 'I grant your wish; it may be that some honour will thereby accrue to your name,' and he bared his shoulders to him as to a friend. Iblis kissed them and vanished from the earth. But from each of Zuhak's shoulders appeared a black serpent, and Zuhak became sick at heart and sought on all sides for a remedy. Finally he bade that the serpents be cut off close to his shoulder, but they grew again. Every physician and wise man in the kingdom tried his remedies, but all in vain. The last to come was Iblis himself, who appeared as a physician before Zuhak. 'It was inevitable', said he, 'that this should happen. Leave the serpents and do not cut them off while there is life in them. To appease them you must feed them on the brains of men, which alone will at last slay them.'

While these events were taking place at the

court of Arabia, great tumults filled the land of
Iran.   The arrogance of Jamshid had set his
subjects in revolt against him, and a great army
marched towards Arabia from the highlands of
Iran.   They had heard that in Arabia there was
a man with a serpent's face that inspired terror in
men, and to him they went in order to elect him as
their king.   Zuhak eagerly returned with them and
was crowned, and, turning his eyes towards the
throne of Jamshid, began to treat the world
familiarly as if it were the ring upon his finger.
Jamshid fled before him, and for a hundred years
was seen by no man, till Zuhak fell upon him
without warning on the confines of China and put
him to death.   Thus perished his pride from the
earth.

For a thousand years Zuhak occupied the throne
and the world submitted to him, so that goodness
died away and was replaced by evil.   Every night
during that long period two youths were slain to
provide the serpents' food.   Now in the king's
country there remained two men of purity, of
Persian race, the one Irmail the Pious, and the
other Girmail the Clear-sighted.   It happened that
they met one day and talked of many matters great
and small; of the unjust king, of his army, and of
his horrible custom.   The one said : ' We ought,
by the art of the kitchen, to introduce ourselves
into the king's household and apply our wits to
saving the unfortunates who lose their lives each
day.'   Setting to work, they learned the art of
cookery, and succeeded in entering the king's
kitchen.   There, after no long time, they were
entrusted with the preparation of the king's meal,
and they contrived to mix the brains of a sheep

with those of one of the youths who was brought
for slaughter. The other one they saved alive and
dismissed secretly, saying to him: 'Escape in
secret, beware of visiting any inhabited town;
your portion in the world must be the desert and
the mountain.'

In this manner they saved two hundred men,
of whom is born the race of Kurds, who know not
any fixed abode, whose houses are tents; and who
have in their hearts no fear of God.

While Zuhak still had forty years to live, one
night he dreamed a dream, and he saw three royal
warriors emerge, two of them aged, and another,
younger, who walked between them, and who had
the form of a cypress and the visage of a king.
His girth and his gait were those of a prince,
and he carried a club with a bull's head. He
advanced straight upon Zuhak, smote him upon
the forehead with his club, tied him hand and
foot with thongs, and overwhelmed him with
shame and torments.

Zuhak awoke with a great cry of fear, that
brought his wife, Arnawaz, and his attendants
running to him in alarm. Arnawaz, as she approached, cried out to him: ' O king, confide in me
and tell me what has happened. You sleep in
your palace securely; everything that is in the
world obeys you; savage beasts, divs, and men
are your guardians; the earth with its seven
climes is your domain; all, from the firmament to
the depth of the seas, is yours. Why then do you
leap thus from your bed? Tell us.' Zuhak
replied: ' My dream must be kept secret, for were
I to reveal it, you would despair of my life.'
' Perhaps, if you reveal it,' said Arnawaz, ' we

may find a remedy, for no ill exists that has not its remedy.' The king was persuaded by this, and told what he had seen in his dream. 'This is not a matter that you may neglect,' exclaimed the queen on hearing it. 'Summon from every country the sages that can read the stars, examine all sources, and seek thus to learn the secret. Discover what he is whose hand threatens you; man, div, or peri; and when you know, then immediately apply your remedy.' And the king approved the counsel of this silver swan.

The world, plunged in night, was black as a raven's wing; suddenly light dawned upon the mountains as though the sun had scattered rubies upon the azure of the firmament. Wherever there were wise counsellors the king sought them out and assembled them in his palace, where he told the whole company of his trouble, and sought their advice. The lips of the noblemen were dried with fear, their cheeks paled, and their hearts filled with anguish. 'For', said each to himself, 'if we disclose what must happen, he will die, and if we remain silent, then we must bid adieu to life.' Thus they remained hesitating for three days. And on the fourth day, Zuhak assembled them again and in rage asked for their counsel, and menaced them with death if they withheld from him their knowledge of the future.

At length there stood out from among the noble counsellors one who was their chief, whose conduct was upright and whose heart was filled with wisdom. He loosened his tongue before Zuhak, and spoke thus: 'Empty thine heart of vain hope, for no one is born save to die. There have been many kings before you worthy of the throne of power, they saw much of grief and much of joy; and, when their long days had flowed past, they died. Were you a rampart of iron securely founded, the turn of the skies would break you too, and you would disappear. There will be some one who will inherit your throne and will overturn your fortunes. His name is Faridun, but he is not yet born, and the time to fear him is not yet. He will grow like a tree destined to bear fruit, and when he has reached manhood his head will touch the moon. Then he will demand your girdle and your crown, your throne and your diadem. He will carry upon his shoulder a club of steel, and with his bull-headed mace he will strike you and drag you from your palace.'

'What reason has he for hating me?' cried out the impure Zuhak.

'Because his father will die at your hands.'

The king heard and thought on this, fell from his throne, and swooned away. When his senses returned to him, he mounted again upon his throne and sent out searchers, both secret and public, to seek for traces of Faridun. He sought no rest or sleep or food, and bright day became gloomy to him.

Thus passed a long space of time, while the serpent-man remained prey to his terror. Faridun was born, and the lot of the whole world was thereby destined to change. The youth grew up like a cypress, and he was resplendent with all the glory of majesty. He was like the shining sun, as needful to the world as rain, an adornment to the mind like knowledge. Zuhak filled the earth with sound and fury, searching everywhere for Faridun son of Abtin. The earth became straitened for

Abtin, who fled and struggled; but he was finally caught in the lion's net.

Meantime Faridun was well secured by his mother, and was safe. The king ceased not night or day to be in anguish concerning him. One day he seated himself on his ivory throne, and, putting his crown upon his head, summoned all his nobles. To them he spoke thus: 'O you men of virtue, noble and prudent, I have a hidden enemy, as all men know. I despise no enemy however feeble, for I fear lest fortune betray me. I must increase my army, and will have it of men, divs, and peris. I desire you to aid me, for I cannot bear my torment alone. You must write for me a declaration that as king I have sown nought but the seed of good, that I have spoken nought save the words of truth, that I have never frustrated justice.' All the noblemen, in fear of the king, consented to his demand, and all, old and young, declared what the serpent-man desired.

But suddenly at the gate of the palace was heard the voice of one crying out for justice. The complainant was brought before the king, who asked who had done him wrong. The man cried out, struck his head with his hands on seeing the monarch, and said: 'I am Kawa, O king; I demand justice. Grant me justice. I have come in haste, and it is you whom I accuse in the bitterness of my heart. I had seventeen sons, and now there remains but one. Give me back this one, my only son; think how my heart will burn with grief, the whole length of my life. What crime have I committed? Even tyranny must have a pretext, and I am an innocent man, a blacksmith. You must render count to me for what you have done, and

the world will be astonished thereby. It will see, by
the account you will render to me, what my lot on
earth has been, and how I have been compelled
to give my sons to feed your serpents.'

The king looked harshly upon him on hearing
these words, gave back the man's son, and strove
to soothe him with words. Lastly he asked Kawa
to sign the declaration of the nobles, but he,
trembling with rage, tore and trampled on it and
emerged shouting with a mighty anger. The
crowd in the market-place gathered round him,
and to them and the whole world he appealed to
aid him in obtaining justice. He took off the
apron which blacksmiths wear, tied it to a lance
and marched through the bazaars crying : ' Illustrious men, you that adore God, who desire to be
delivered from the clutches of Zuhak, let us go
to Faridun and let us rest in the shadow of his
sovereignty.'

Having ascertained where Faridun lay hiding,
he set out with a great troop of men, and after no
long time reached his abode. The young prince saw
the standard made of the blacksmith's apron, and
accepted it as a good omen. Then, tarrying only
while a suit of armour was made for him, he began
his march at the head of his army, which moved
as speedily as the wind. Soon they reached the
Tigris river and the city of Baghdad. Arrived
there, Faridun sent his greeting to the guardian of
the crossing, and said : ' Send me boats and ships,
that I and my army may cross.' But the guardian
sent back answer : ' The king has given me secret
command that no man may cross without his sealed
order.'

Faridun heard the messenger with anger. The

swift stream inspired him with no fear, and he with his warriors tightened girdle and plunged into it with their horses. Having crossed, they made their way to the royal city of Zuhak. On coming within a mile of it Faridun saw a palace whose walls were raised higher than Saturn, as if it had been built to tear the stars from the sky. It shone like Jupiter in the celestial sphere. From its vastness and magnificence Faridun knew it to be the palace of the monster-king, and, turning to his companions, he said : ' I fear one that has been able from dust and stones to rear so mighty a structure. I fear some secret bond between fortune and him, but it is better to fling ourselves into battle than to delay here.' Thus he spoke, and, giving rein to his spirited horse, he raised his club and rushed like a flame past the wardens of the gate and into the palace. He dashed to the ground a talisman which Zuhak had set up against him, and struck down all that offered resistance ; he placed his foot upon the throne of Zuhak, seized the royal crown, and took his place.

A servant of Zuhak saw what had happened, and mounting a swift horse brought the tale to his master: ' O king of a proud people, there are tokens that portend the fall of your fortunes. Three heroes have come from a strange land with an army. The youngest remains always between the two elder, his stature is that of a prince, his face that of a king. He carries a mighty club like a great rock, and he has seated himself upon the throne.'

Zuhak, in great haste, prepared to return with an army of divs and men. By devious ways he flung his army against the terraces and gates of the palace, thinking of nought but vengeance. But the army of Faridun and the inhabitants of the town fought together in the battle, and their mass was like a mountain.

Meantime rage incited Zuhak to further enterprise. Covering himself from head to foot with armour, that none might know him, in the confusion he climbed unseen into the palace by means of a rope of sixty cubits. But he was recognized and pursued and, in his rage, leapt from the battlements to the ground. Faridun advanced, swift as the wind, and smote Zuhak with his club through his helmet to his head. But a faithful counsellor held his hand, saying, ' His time is not yet come. He is broken but not dead. Let him be placed to spend the rest of his days in the depths of the rocks, where neither his friends nor his vassals can find him.'

So Faridun prepared thongs of lion skin, and bound Zuhak's hands and feet and body, in such manner that a wild elephant could not have broken the bonds. He bore the monster, thus tightly bound, to the height of the lofty mountain of Damawand, and there, in a narrow bottomless chasm, he chained him. And there Zuhak remains suspended until the ill he wrought shall have vanished from the earth.

[From the *Shah-nama.*]

THE STORY OF THE SAILOR
AND THE PEARL MERCHANT

IT is related that in the city of Basrah there was
a man, Abu'l Fawaris, who was the chief of the
sailors of the town, for in the great ocean there
was no port at which he had not landed. One day,
as he sat on the seashore, with his sailors round
him, an old man arrived in a ship, landed where
Abu'l Fawaris was sitting, and said : 'Friend,
I desire you to give me your ship for six months,
and I will pay you whatever you desire.' 'I demand a thousand gold dinars,' said the sailor, and
at once received the gold from the old man, who,
before departing, said that he would come again
on the next day, and warned Abu'l Fawaris that
there was to be no holding back.

The sailor took home his gold, made his ship
ready, and then, taking leave of his wife and sons,
he went down to the shore, where he found the old
man waiting for him with a slave and twenty ass-
loads of empty sacks. Abu'l Fawaris greeted him,
and together they loaded the ship and set sail.
Taking a particular star for their mark, they sailed
for three months, when an island appeared to one
side of them. For this the old man steered, and
they soon landed upon it. Having loaded his slave
with some sacks, the old man with his companions
set out towards a mountain which they could see
in the distance. This they reached after some
hours of travel, and climbed to the summit, upon
which they found a broad plain where more than

two hundred pits had been dug. The old man then explained to the sailor that he was a merchant, and that he had, on that spot, found a mine of jewels. 'Now that I have given you my confidence,' he continued, 'I expect faithfulness from you too. I desire you to go down into this pit and send up sufficient pearls to fill these sacks. Half I will give to you, and we shall be able to spend the rest of our lives in luxury.' The sailor thereupon asked how the pearls had found their way into these pits, to which the old man replied that there was a passage connecting the pits with the sea. Along this passage oysters swam, and settled in the pits, where by chance he had come upon them. He explained further that he had only brought the sailor because he needed help; but he desired not to disclose the matter to any one else.

With great eagerness then the sailor descended into the pit, and there found oysters in great numbers. The old man let down a basket to him, which he filled again and again, until at last the merchant cried out that the oysters were useless, for they contained no pearls. Abu'l Fawaris therefore left that pit, and descended into another, where he found pearls in great number. By the time night fell he was utterly wearied, and called out to the old man to help him out of the pit. In reply the merchant shouted down that he intended to leave him in the pit, for he feared that Abu'l Fawaris might kill him for the sake of the jewels. With great vehemence the sailor protested that he was innocent of any such intention, but the old man was deaf to his entreaties, and, making his way back to the ship, sailed away.

For three days Abu'l Fawaris remained, hungry

and thirsty. As he struggled to find a way out he came upon many human bones, and understood that the accursed old man had betrayed many others in the same fashion. In desperation he dug about, and at last he saw a small opening, which he enlarged with his hands. Soon it was big enough for him to crawl through, and he found himself in the darkness, standing upon mud. Along this he walked carefully, and then felt himself suddenly plunged to his neck in water, which was salt to the taste; and he knew that he was in the passage that led to the sea. He swam along in this for some way, till, in front of him, there appeared a faint light. Greatly heartened by the sight of it, he swam vigorously until he reached the mouth of the passage. On emerging, he found himself facing the sea, and threw himself on his face to give thanks for his delivery. Then he arose, and a little distance from him he found the cloak which he had left behind when he set out for the mountain; but of the old merchant there was no sign, and the ship had disappeared.

Full of trouble and despondency, he sat down at the water's brink, wondering what he was to do. As he gazed at the sea there came into view a ship, and he saw that it was filled with men. At sight of it the sailor leapt from his place; snatching his turban from his head, he waved it with all his might in the air, and shouted at the top of his voice. But as they approached he decided not to tell his rescuers the truth of his presence there; therefore when they landed and asked how he came to be on the island he told them that his ship had been wrecked at sea, that he had clung to a plank and been washed to the shore.

They praised his good fortune at his escape, and in reply to his questions with regard to the place of their origin, told him that they had sailed from Abyssinia, and were then on their way to Hindustan. At this, Abu'l Fawaris hesitated, saying that he had no business in Hindustan. They assured him, however, that they would meet ships going to Basrah, and would hand him over to one of them. He agreed then to go with them, and for forty days they sailed without seeing any inhabited spot. At last he asked them whether they had not mistaken their way, and they admitted that for five days they had been sailing without knowing whither they were going or what direction to follow. All together therefore set themselves to praying, and remained in prayer for some time.

Soon afterwards, as they sailed, something in appearance like a minaret emerged from the sea, and they seemed to behold the flash of a Chinese mirror. Also they perceived that their ship, without their rowing, and without any greater force of wind, began to move at great speed over the water. In great amazement the sailors ran to Abu'l Fawaris and asked him what had come to the ship that it moved so fast. He raised his eyes, and groaned deeply as in the distance he saw a mountain that rose out of the sea. In terror he clapped his hand to his eyes and shouted out : ' We shall all perish ! My father continually warned me that if ever I lost my way upon the sea I must steer to the East ; for if I went to the West I would certainly fall into the Lion's Mouth. When I asked him what the Lion's Mouth was, he told me that the Almighty had created a great hole in the midst of the ocean, at the foot of a mountain. That is the Lion's Mouth. Over a hundred leagues of water it will attract a ship, and no vessel which encounters the mountain ever rises again. I believe that this is the place and that we are caught.'

In great terror the sailors saw their ship being carried like the wind against the mountain. Soon it was caught in the whirlpool, where the wrecks of ten thousand ancient ships were being carried around in the swirling current. The sailors and merchants in the ship crowded to Abu'l Fawaris, begging him to tell them what they could do. He cried out to them to prepare all the ropes which they had in the ship ; he would then swim out of the whirlpool and on to the shore at the foot of the mountain, where he would make fast to some stout tree. Then they were to cast their ropes to him and so he would rescue them from their peril. By great good fortune the current cast him out upon the shore, and he made the rope of his ship fast to a stout tree.

Then, as soon as was possible, the sailor climbed to the top of the mountain in search of food, for neither he nor his shipmates had eaten for some days. When he reached the summit he found a pleasant plain stretching away in front of him, and in the midst of it he saw a lofty arch, made of green stone. As he approached it and entered, he observed a tall pillar made of steel, from which there hung by a chain a great drum of Damascus bronze covered with a lion's skin. From the arch also hung a great tablet of bronze, upon which was engraved the following inscription : ' O thou that dost reach this place, know that when Alexander voyaged round the world and reached the Lion's

Mouth, he had been made aware of this place of calamity. He was therefore accompanied by four thousand wise men, whom he summoned and whom he commanded to provide a means of escape from this calamitous spot. For long the philosophers pondered on the matter, until at last Plato caused this drum to be made, whose quality is that if any one, being caught in the whirlpool, can come forth and strike the drum three times, he will bring out his ship to the surface.'

When the sailor had read the inscription, he quickly made his way to the shore and told his fellows of it. After much debate he agreed to risk his life by staying on the island and striking the drum, on condition that they would return to Basrah on their escape, and give to his wife and sons one-half of what treasure they had in the ship. He bound them with an oath to do this, and then returned to the arch. Taking up a club he struck the drum three times, and as the mighty roar of it echoed from the hills, the ship, like an arrow shot from a bow, was flung out of the whirlpool. Then, with a cry of farewell to Abu'l Fawaris from the crew, they sailed to Basrah, where they gave one-half the treasure which they had to the sailor's family.

With great mourning the wife and family of Abu'l Fawaris celebrated his loss; but he, after sleeping soundly in the archway and giving thanks to his Maker for preserving him alive, made his way again to the summit of the mountain. As he advanced across the plain he saw black smoke arising from it, and also in the plain were rivers, of which he passed nine. He was like to die of hunger and weariness, when suddenly he perceived on one side a meadow, in which flocks of sheep were grazing. In great joy he thought that he was at last reaching human habitation, and as he came towards the sheep, he saw with them a youth, tall in stature as a mountain, and covered with a tattered cloak of red felt, though his head and body were clad in mail. The sailor greeted him, and received greeting in reply, and also the question 'Whence come you?' Abu'l Fawaris answered that he was a man upon whom catastrophe had fallen, and so related his adventures to the shepherd. He heard it with a laugh, and said: 'Count yourself fortunate to have escaped from that abyss. Do not fear now, I will bring you to a village.' Saying this he set bread and milk before him and bade him eat. When he had eaten he said: 'You cannot remain here all day, I will take you to my house, where you may rest for a time.'

Together they descended to the foot of the mountain, where stood a gateway. Against it leaned a mighty stone, which a hundred men could not have lifted, but the shepherd, putting his hand into a hole in the stone, lifted it away from the gateway and admitted Abu'l Fawaris. Then he restored the stone to its place, and continued his way.

When the sailor had passed through the gateway he saw before him a beautiful garden in which were trees laden with fruit. In the midst of them was a kiosk, and this, the sailor thought, must be the shepherd's house. He entered and looked about from the roof, but though he saw many houses there was no person in sight. He descended therefore, and walked to the nearest house, which he entered. Upon crossing the threshold he beheld

ten men, all naked and all so fat that their eyes
were almost closed. With their heads down upon
their knees, all were weeping bitterly. But at the
sound of his footsteps they raised their heads and
called out 'Who are you?' He told them that the
shepherd had brought him and offered him hospitality. A great cry arose from them as they heard
this. 'Here', they said, 'is another unfortunate
who has fallen, like ourselves, into the clutch of
this monster. He is a vile creature, who in the
guise of a shepherd goes about and seizes men and
devours them. We are all merchants whom
adverse winds have brought here. That div has
seized us and keeps us in this fashion.'

With a groan the sailor thought that now at last
he was undone. At that moment he saw the
shepherd coming, saw him let the sheep into the
garden, and then close the gateway with the stone
before entering the kiosk. He was carrying a bag
full of almonds, dates, and pistachio nuts, with
which he approached, and, giving it to the sailor, he
told him to share it with the others. Abu'l Fawaris
could say nothing, but sat down and ate the food
with his companions. When they had finished their
meal, the shepherd returned to them, took one of
them by the hand, and then in sight of them all,
slew, roasted, and devoured him. When he was
sated, he brought out a skin of wine and drank
until he fell into a drunken sleep.

Then the sailor turned to his companions and
said : 'Since I am to die, let me first destroy him ;
if you will give me your help, I will do so.' They
replied that they had no strength left ; but he,
seeing the two long spits on which the ogre had
roasted his meat, put them into the fire until they

were red hot, and then plunged them into the monster's eyes.

With a great cry the shepherd leapt up and tried to seize his tormentor, who sprang away and eluded him. Running to the stone, the shepherd moved it aside and began to let out the sheep one by one, in the hope that when the garden was emptier he could the more easily capture the sailor. Abu'l Fawaris understood his intention: without delay, he slew a sheep, put on the skin and tried to pass through. But the shepherd knew as soon as he felt him that this was not a sheep, and leapt after him in pursuit. Abu'l Fawaris flung off the pelt, and ran like the wind. Soon he came to the sea, and into this he plunged, while the shepherd after a few steps returned to the shore, for he could not swim.

Full of terror the sailor swam till he reached the other side of the mountain. There he met an old man who greeted him, and, after hearing his adventure, fed him and took him to his house. But soon, to his horror, Abu'l Fawaris found that this old man also was an ogre. With great cunning he told the ogre's wife that he could make many useful implements for her house, and she persuaded her husband to save him. After many days in the house, he was sent away to the care of a shepherd, and put to guard sheep. Day by day he planned to escape, but there was only one way across the mountain and that was guarded.

One day, as he wandered in a wood, he found in the hollow trunk of a tree a store of honey, of which he told the shepherd's wife when he went home. The next day, therefore, the woman sent her husband with Abu'l Fawaris, telling him to bring

home some of the honey; but, on the way, the
sailor leapt upon him and bound him to a tree.
Then, taking the shepherd's ring, he returned and
told the woman that her husband had given him
leave to go, and that he sent his ring in token of
this. But the woman was cunning and asked:
' Why did not my husband come himself to tell
me this ? ' Seizing him by the cloak, she told him
that she would go with him and find out the truth.
The sailor, however, tore himself free, and again
fled to the sea, where he thought that he might
escape death. In haste and terror he swam for
many hours, until at last he espied a ship full of
men, who steered towards him and took him on
board. Full of wonder they asked how he came
there, and he related to them all his adventures.

It happened by great good fortune that the
ship's captain had business at one place only on
the coast, and that from there he was sailing to
Basrah. In the space of a month, therefore, Abu'l
Fawaris was restored to his family, to the joy of
them all.

The many dangers and sufferings of the sailor
had turned his hair white. For many days he
rested, and then, one day, as he walked by the
sea-shore, that same old man who had before hired
his ship again appeared. Without recognizing
him, he asked if he would lend his ship on hire for
six months. Abu'l Fawaris agreed to do so for
a thousand dinars of gold, which the old man at
once paid to him, saying that he would come in
a boat on the morrow, ready to depart.

When the ancient departed, the sailor took
home the money to his wife, who bade him beware
not to cast himself again into danger. He replied

that he must be avenged not only for himself, but also for the thousand Muslims whom the villainous old man had slain.

The next day, therefore, the sailor took on board the old man and a black slave, and for three months they sailed, until they once more reached the island of pearls. There they made fast the ship on the shore, and taking sacks, they ascended to the top of the mountain. Once arrived there, the old man made the same request to Abu'l Fawaris as before, namely, that he should go down into the pits and send up pearls. The sailor replied that he was unacquainted with the place, and preferred that the old man should go down first, in order to prove that there was no danger. He answered that there was surely no danger; he had never in his life harmed even an ant, and he would of a certainty never send Abu'l Fawaris down into the pits if he knew any peril lay there. But the sailor was obstinate, saying that until he knew how to carry it out, he could not undertake the task.

Very reluctantly, therefore, the old man allowed himself to be lowered into the first pit by a basket and a rope. He filled the basket with oysters and sent it up, crying out: 'You see, there is nothing to do harm in this pit. Draw me up now, for I am an old man and have no more strength left.' The sailor replied, 'Now that you are there, it were better if you remained there to complete your task. To-morrow I myself will go into another pit and will send up so many pearls as to fill the ship.' For a long time the old man worked, sending up pearls, and at last he cried out again 'O my brother, I am utterly wearied, draw me out now.' Then the sailor turned upon him with fury, and cried out:

' How is it that thou dost see ever thine own trouble and never that of others ? Thou misbegotten dog, art thou blind that thou dost not know me ? I am Abu'l Fawaris the sailor, whom long ago you left in one of these pits. By the favour of Allah I was delivered, and now it is your turn. Open your eyes to the truth and remember what you have done to so many men.' The old man cried aloud for mercy, but it availed him nothing, for Abu'l Fawaris brought a great stone and covered up the mouth of the pit. The slave too he overwhelmed with threats, and then together they carried down the pearls to the ship, in which they set sail. In three months they arrived at Basrah. There Abu'l Fawaris related his adventures, to the amazement of all. Thenceforward he abandoned the sea and adopted a life of ease. Finally he died, and this story remains in memory of him. And Allah knoweth best.

[MS. Ouseley 231, fol. 167ª ff.]

THE TREASURE OF MANSUR

THERE was once a prince of Baghdad, famed for his richness and the vastness of his treasures. He had one son, Mansur, whom he loved dearly, and whom he had reared with the greatest care. He engaged the wisest philosophers and the most learned tutors to teach him, so that he understood the languages of east and west. With the passage of time, the prince became aware that the day of his death was near. Therefore, summoning Mansur, he spoke to him as follows : ' My son, I am about to depart and you will be left alone to deal with the great treasures which I bequeath to you. Spend it not except by measure, and ponder well on all you do.'

The next day the prince died, and Mansur mourned for him. So eager, however, was he to behold his father's treasures that at the end of three days he cast off his mourning, and, taking the keys of the treasure-house with him, he made his way into it. He remained astonished at the sight of the gold and jewels which were heaped there, and thought to himself : ' Why did my father warn me so earnestly, for here is more than I can ever spend ? ' He therefore commanded his servants to bring out chests full of gold and jewels, and the next day he set about planning the building of gardens and palaces which would excel in splendour all that had ever been built before. His gardens were filled with the finest fruit-trees, and under each was set a couch of precious wood inlaid with gold and jewels.

Thus Mansur continued, until at last his treasure-houses were empty. By degrees he was compelled to sell his gardens and fine houses until only one remained, and soon he decided that he would sell this too. With the money he would buy merchandise and travel into foreign countries, where he could acquire wealth again.

This he did. He sold his last house, loaded a caravan, and set out for Mosul, where he arrived after a long journey. He found it a fine city with splendid palaces and pleasant gardens, but his business there did not prosper. After a month he decided to travel farther to Syria, and accordingly, leaving Mosul with a caravan, he journeyed from city to city until Damascus was reached. He found a town full of people, surrounded by beautiful gardens and containing many great buildings. Filled with delight, he remained in the town until his merchandise was all sold and the money he had obtained for it was all eaten up. Then he departed, leaving on foot with a caravan, and gaining a livelihood by bringing water for sale to merchants at any place where they alighted.

It happened one day that he fell sick; his clothes were worn out and he had no money wherewith to buy food. Faint and weak after a long journey, he fell down in the bazaar of a town where he had arrived. A crowd gathered round him, and took pity on him when they saw that he was young and a foreigner. They offered him food and drink, but he refused it, until one, more wealthy and understanding than the rest, took him to the hammam, and gave him clothes and brought him to his house. There Mansur ate and drank, and related his history to his benefactor.

When he had concluded, his host asked him whither he now intended to go, and he replied that he wished to go to Egypt. This kindly man, therefore, gave him a sum of gold for his journey and dismissed him, praying that God would favour him with fortune.

Mansur set his face towards Egypt, and after a long journey arrived in the great city of Cairo. There he beheld a magnificent spectacle of great bazaars and rich shops ; on every side were palaces reaching into the blue sky. On both banks of the Nile were fine buildings and beautiful gardens. For long he marvelled, and with the money that remained to him he bought such delectable foods as his heart desired. Many days he wandered in the bazaars, beholding and marvelling at the people and the palaces. It happened that every day he passed by a place on the river-side where women draw water, and there was one that came regularly and greatly pleased Mansur by her appearance. One day he made acquaintance with her, and for several days afterwards he met her at the watering place. Then one day as he came she saw that he was downcast and gloomy, and, when she asked the reason, he told her that his money was almost at an end, and that he did not know how he was to live in the future. She said to him : 'Many people pass by here bent on pleasure. Buy some fruits and sweetmeats and lay them in a tray or on the grass. I, too, will help you and give you food. When people sit down here to eat, enter into conversation with them, amuse them with witticisms and become friendly with them.' Mansur approved of this plan. That very moment he departed, and brought fruits and sweets and offered them to people that came down to the water.

This he continued to do for some time, so that people became well acquainted with him and always bought from him, and every night he carried home a sum of money. One day, two Indians, richly dressed, came to sit down near him. They called to him to bring them some of his wares, and he set his tray before them. They made him sit down with them, telling him to remain with them to amuse them for the whole day, and not to go to any one else. Mansur said that he would place himself at their service, and sat down with them to eat and drink.

Very soon the two Indians were drunk, and, holding out some gold dinars, told Mansur to play and sing and amuse them with stories. When at last they were too dazed with wine to hear more, they began to speak to each other in the Indian tongue, not knowing that Mansur could understand them. He heard one of them say, ' The gold which we brought is finished, we must go out to-night and find sufficient for our needs.' The other, however, replied : ' No, I brought enough for a month.' This filled Mansur with the thought that the two men must in some place have a store of gold, and he therefore determined to discover what further information he could concerning the two men, and so find out whence they got their gold and their wealth. He remained in their company until one hour after sunset, then taking up the accoutrement which they had brought with them, they departed.

Mansur hastened to his friend and told her that he intended to go to his own lodging that night. ' The way is long,' said he, ' and if you have a

sword I pray you give it to me.' The woman gave
him a sword, and Mansur hastened away in pursuit
of the two men. He followed them outside the
town and into the desert. There they sat down,
and he heard them say to each other that they
must go warily and see that no one followed them.
Mansur at this crept into a hole which he found,
fortunately for himself, for one of the two Indians
turned back a little way to see if any one was
about. Again they proceeded until they reached
a certain tree, under which they halted. Mansur
saw them engaged in digging for a little while,
then suddenly they disappeared from view. Very
cautiously he approached and at last he saw the
mouth of a hole, and, inside it, a door. He was just
about to descend, when one of the Indians appeared
with a bag upon his back. As soon as he emerged
Mansur sprang upon him with his sword and
hacked off his head. The bag fell to the ground,
but as Mansur was about to bend down to open it,
the other Indian appeared, also carrying a bag.
Swiftly Mansur turned upon him, sword in hand,
and slew him too. Then he opened both bags and
found them filled with pearls.

In great haste he descended into the hole
and beheld before him a vestibule, very long and
dark. As he proceeded along it, it began to grow
lighter, and he made his way towards the spot
whence the light came. Soon he beheld an
enormous palace, in the midst of which was a great
fountain surrounded by ten gold pillars, orna-
mented with jewels. By each pillar was set
a jewel-encrusted throne and great vats full of
jewels and wealth beyond counting. Being driven
almost to madness by what he had seen, Mansur

rushed out into the open, locking the door after him. Then, taking up the two bags, which he had filled with gold coins, he made his way back to his lodging.

The next day Mansur set about spending his newly-gotten wealth. Summoning his neighbours, he bought from them at a great price all the houses in that district, and there began to build a palace, the like of which no prince or vizier in all Egypt possessed. When it was completed, he had it spread with carpets befitting its richness. Night after night he went to the underground palace and brought back some of the treasure. But if one man had worked night and day for a thousand years he could never have completed the task.

At last the people of Cairo began to talk among themselves about Mansur, and said: 'This Baghdadi, who used to sell fruits and sweets and to wander from tavern to tavern, is now richer than any one in Cairo, though there are many owners of great treasure here. Whence does he acquire all the wealth to enable him to build so fine a palace and maintain his household so lavishly? Also, does he pay his due tenth to the prince of Cairo?' This talk reached the ears of the chief of the police, who thereupon made his way to the palace of Mansur. He was amazed at the sight that met his gaze, and, turning to Mansur, he said: 'The people of this city remember that when you came here you were a beggar, but now your affairs have reached this prosperous state. Will you not inform me whence you have obtained all this wealth and splendour? Whatever it be, I bid you tell me the truth.' When Mansur asked him what office he held, he replied that he was chief of the police. This

alarmed Mansur greatly, and he was much agitated.
The officer, however, told him not to be afraid, and
added that if Mansur dealt generously with him,
he in his turn would be generous also. ' How much
must I pay ? ' asked Mansur. When he was told
a hundred dirhams of silver he laughed aloud,
and offered a hundred dinars of gold, whereat the
officer was much pleased, and said : ' Even if you
have found a hundred treasures you are welcome
to them, in so far as concerns me.'

Soon afterwards the story reached the ears of
the vizier also. He summoned Mansur, and,
treating him with great regard, said : ' I understand that when you came here you were a beggar,
penniless and friendless, but that now you have
become possessed of great treasure. It has come
to our sovereign's ears that the royal dues are not
being paid by you. I advise you therefore, my
friend, to pay these dues ; but, in addition, you
may expend what you please.'

Upon hearing this, Mansur understood what
was expected of him, and said : ' I admit that
I have found a treasure, but it is in a place where
no man can cast an eye. I am a foreigner and will
not pay a grain to the Sultan, even if he tears me
limb from limb ; but to you I will pay a thousand
dirhams every day, and that is sufficient to defray
all the expenditure of Cairo. I say this, however,
on condition that you are content with what I pay
and do not demand more.' The vizier swore an
oath that he would not demand more, thinking
that if he slew Mansur he would derive no profit.
He therefore dismissed him, saying : ' For my
part, if you have found a thousand treasures you
are welcome to them.' But he sent a messenger

to Mansur to bring back the first day's payment.

Some time elapsed and then the story of the treasure was brought to the Sultan. He summoned the vizier and asked him concerning Mansur, and then he called Mansur before him. He treated him with great condescension, and said : ' Young man, if you discover to me this treasure which you have found, I will take but one fifth of it and leave the rest to you.' Mansur replied : ' An oath has been laid upon me not to disclose my secret to a living soul, and if I were to be cut into a thousand pieces I would not speak of it. I will pay, however, daily, the sum of twelve thousand dinars in gold.' The matter was thus arranged, and the Sultan bade the vizier to put on Mansur a robe of honour, and to publish his name abroad with great ceremony as a public benefactor.

When Mansur had departed, the Sultan began to consider how great the treasure of Mansur must be if he could afford to pay twelve thousand dinars every day in addition to other great sums. He pondered long, therefore, on the means whereby he could lay his hands on the source of this wealth. As he sat thus engrossed in thought, a favourite slave-girl beheld him and asked what schemes possessed him. He told her what he had in mind, and she replied that she would gain for him what he desired. He promised that if she succeeded he would give her one of his palaces for her own, and would keep her with him always.

Now it happened that Mansur's custom was to sit in his courtyard every day, with a chest of gold by his side. Beggars and other needy persons came in streams to ask his aid, and, being given

what they desired, passed on. On the day after
Mansur had visited the Sultan, a maiden joined the
stream of people at Mansur's house, and, as she
passed by him, she uncovered her face and smiled
at him bewitchingly, saying that she had a request
to make in private. Mansur, greatly delighted
with her beauty, bade her go into the house, and
he followed. There he bade food and wine to be
brought, and, while they ate and drank, Mansur
became more and more enamoured of her. At last
he asked what her need was, and she replied : ' I
have heard that you have found a rich treasure,
and I am consumed with desire to behold it.'
Mansur laughed aloud at this, but after much
persuasion he at last consented. He put on a cloak,
took a sword, and bade the girl accompany him.
When they arrived outside the city, he blindfolded
his companion securely with a kerchief, and led her
to the underground chamber. There he uncovered
her eyes again and showed her all that there was
to see. She was amazed at the sight, and said,
' Show me whence you obtain all the gold coins
which you pay out every day.' He pointed to the
tank, which was full of gold coins up to two fingers'
breadth from the top. ' Here ', he said, ' I have
sufficient to last me the whole of my life, and need
never touch the rest of the treasure.'

After going about for some time, Mansur and
his companion desired to rest, and they proceeded
towards an alcove where there stood a couch. As
they entered they saw another couch on one side,
and upon it a man asleep, with a maiden by his
side. Over the head of the sleeping man hung a
golden tablet, upon which was written : ' I, that
gathered all this treasure, took cities, and stormed

fortresses, and overcame all mine enemies. When death descended upon me, this wealth was of no avail to me that created it. If it falls into the hand of any man, let him spend it lavishly, for it will not diminish. In me, that gathered it all, desires are at an end. Let him that beholds me be warned, and let him not be deceived by worldly wealth.'

After reading this Mansur looked again at the sleeping pair, and saw that they were dead. Around the dead maiden's neck was a necklace of jewels. This Mansur unclasped and gave it to his companion, whose eyes he again covered with the kerchief. This time she cried out, and begged that she might be allowed to see where she was going. But Mansur asked her if she was tired of life that she spoke thus, and she remained silent.

They then returned to the city, Mansur going to his home, and the slave-girl back to the palace. There she told the Sultan all that had occurred and confessed her failure. In great wrath thereat he told her to go back to Mansur, to whom he said he had presented her. When she arrived, Mansur bid her to rejoice, for he would deal with her a thousand times more graciously than ever her royal master had done. With great ceremony he married her, and with her lived long and happily. But, when he died, he told the secret of his treasure to no one, so that it disappeared from the world.

[MS. Ouseley 187, page 187 (margin).]

THE PALACE OF NINE
PAVILIONS

THERE was once a king of Darband, named Karkin, famed for his goodness and power. He had but one sorrow, that he lacked a son. One day, while he was hunting in the forest, he was sorely wounded by a wild boar. As he lay dying he summoned his two viziers, Bihzad and Farsbahram, and told them, that if a son was born to him after he was dead, then that son should succeed him; if not, then Bihzad should reign in his stead.

Now Bihzad was a man full of ambition, and he decided that he would seize the throne even though the queen might bear a son. Immediately on Karkin's death he proclaimed himself ruler of Darband, and, summoning Farsbahram, whom he appointed to be his vizier, told him to take the queen into a neighbouring forest, where there were many lions, and there leave her. Farsbahram obeyed, and led the queen away from the palace. Returning next day to see what had happened, he found her lying dead with a new-born infant beside her. The vizier, taking the child, wrapped it in part of its mother's cloak, took pen and paper, and wrote its history; then, leaving the message and putting a necklace of jewels around the infant's neck, he returned unseen to the palace.

Soon afterwards a lion and lioness came upon the child, and, seeing it crying, took pity on it and fed it. They decided to keep it and bring it up with their own cubs, and with them the babe grew until it was three years old.

At that time there lived in Baghdad a rich merchant named Asad. On his way home with his servants one day, after a long journey, he arrived at the forest, and, finding it a pleasant spot, decided to spend the night there. He dismounted and sent out ten of his servants to bring him game. While they were away his men found the forest infested with lions, and returned in great fright to tell their master. Immediately Asad sent out a hundred servants, who went to the spot where the lions had been seen, gave chase, and finally killed all of them except one lioness. She was found to be carrying on her back a little boy, who, when they tried to take him away, burst into tears and clung to his foster-mother. When at length they succeeded in parting them and examined the child more closely, they found that he was wearing the necklace of jewels which had been put round his neck at birth and also the roll of paper, which had remained untouched.

It can be imagined how great was Asad's astonishment when he unrolled the paper and discovered how the child had been born in the wood. On reading his strange history, the merchant decided to bring him up with the greatest care ; then, ordering his caravan to move on again, set out for Baghdad. The lioness followed quietly at a distance, not attempting to do any one any harm, and the child, seeing her, kept close to her, so that the people of the caravan, realizing their affection for each other, allowed them to travel thus until the end of the journey.

On their arrival at Baghdad the lioness returned

to the forest. The merchant told his wife of his
adventures, and of how he had found the king's
son. She was overcome with delight and lavished
caresses upon the lad, and they decided to call him
Shirzad, which means 'Lion-born'. So Shirzad
grew to manhood, surrounded by all manner of
luxury and gifted with many talents, but in
complete ignorance of his royal birth.

Turn we now to the wicked vizier Bihzad, who,
when the queen had been taken away into the
forest, thought himself secure and established
himself upon the throne.

It happened that Bihzad had a very beautiful
daughter, to whom he gave the name Gulshad,
and whom he loved very dearly. When Gulshad
was grown up, her father called his vizier and said:
'I wish to build a fine palace for Gulshad, one
which shall become famous throughout the world,
and I desire you to find for me the most skilled
craftsman possible to build it.' The vizier made
inquiries everywhere, and at last found in China
a famous builder called Ti Fu, who consented to
come to Darband. There he built an exquisite
palace and surrounded it with a beautiful garden
in which he placed nine pavilions, each named
after the star under which it stood. In each of
these pavilions the princess lived in turn, and
often amused herself by riding on horseback with
her friends.

Now the merchant Asad at Baghdad was
a hospitable man, and welcomed to his house all
the men from foreign lands whose business brought
them to the city. His greatest pleasure was to
hear them tell of their adventures, and one day one
of them told him of the palace at Darband, with its

nine pavilions. Shirzad was in the room when this was told, and at once the desire came to him to go to Darband to see this wonderful place. The merchant told him that he would shortly be going there, and would take him as his companion. Before long, they had laden their animals with merchandise and set off. At the end of several days' march they arrived in the land of the king of Darband, and, by chance, dismounted exactly in the spot in the forest where Asad had first met Shirzad.

One morning, when Shirzad went out into the forest with two or three slaves to hunt, he came upon a lion, which he slew. When he had penetrated still further into the forest he caught sight of a lioness, and was making ready to attack when he saw that she was approaching him without anger or thought of doing him harm. Shirzad soon recognized her as his foster-mother, and began to caress her. Finally, seating himself upon her back, he rode back again to the place where the caravan had encamped. His adopted father and his friends were much amazed at the sight, but Shirzad explained who the lioness was, and delivered her over to Asad.

The next day Shirzad again set out on horseback into the forest, and it chanced that that same day the princess Gulshad herself had left her palace of Nine Pavilions, to hunt with her followers in the forest. The two companies made for the same spot among the trees, and espied each other from afar. As they approached, Shirzad could see several beautiful ladies, mounted on horseback and enjoying the chase, while Gulshad, on seeing the company of gallant horsemen, sent one of her officers

towards them to inquire who they were. The
officer, on approaching the prince, saw in him a
youth beautiful as the rising sun on a clear morning.
He saluted him, and asked : ' Who are you, sir, and
whence do you come ? ' Shirzad satisfied him with
great frankness, and added : ' I have told you very
willingly who we are, and now I hope you in return
will do me the honour to tell me who you are, who
are these ladies whom I see, and what they are
doing here.' ' These ladies,' replied the officer,
' are the princess Gulshad, daughter of King
Bihzad, and her followers, who have come here to
hunt. The princess lives in a palace near by called
the Nine Pavilions, to which belongs a famous
garden. It is her pleasure every three days to
ride out from the palace in pursuit of game.' He
ended his description with such great praise of the
princess that Shirzad became possessed of the
greatest desire to see and to become acquainted
with her.

The officer then withdrew, and returned to the
princess to give an account of what he had learned.
He spoke to her of Shirzad's beauty, of his courtesy
and his gracious bearing, in terms which enchanted
Gulshad. She returned to the Nine Pavilions, and
her thoughts were all that day occupied with
Shirzad. Similarly Shirzad's mind dwelt continually on Gulshad, and each spent the night dreaming of the other.

The next day Gulshad again set out to hunt, and
rode to the same place in the forest where she had
seen Shirzad. There she dismounted. She ordered
a feast to be prepared and commanded cup-bearers
to serve only the finest wine in cups of purest silver.

Shirzad, too, being full of desire to see the

princess again, in spite of his father's words of
caution against the dangers of the forest, set forth,
and at last came to the spot where the princess
was seated. She invited him to the feast, and he
gladly joined her. When it was time to depart,
Gulshad said to her guest : ' You must know that
not far from here I have a dwelling-place com-
parable only to an earthly paradise ; it is known
as the Nine Pavilions, and the world holds nothing
more beautiful. Come with me and remain awhile.'
She urged him with kind words, and at last he
replied : ' Princess, your beauty rivals that of the
Peris ; when you command I must obey. To do
your bidding overwhelms me with joy.' So they
mounted and rode away to Nine Pavilions. From
the hour of their arrival their time was filled with
brilliant assemblies, with feasts and joy and
pleasures. And Shirzad, roaming through the
palace, forgot, in his delight, the outer world.

Now one of the princess's gardeners was deeply
in love with her, and, seeing Shirzad with her, was
consumed with jealous rage. He determined to
go and tell the king of what he had seen, so that
this dangerous rival might be removed from his
path. As soon as day dawned, he went to the
palace in Darband and told Bihzad that a young
man had arrived at the palace of Nine Pavilions,
and was spending all his time feasting and revelling
in the company of Princess Gulshad.

The report inflamed Bihzad with anger. He had
two faithful officers, one named Almas, the other
Katmas ; these he summoned, and said : ' Go at
once with this man to the palace of Nine Pavilions ;
there he will point out to you a man whom I bid
you arrest and bring back here, with his hands

bound and a rope around his neck.' At this
command the two officers mounted their horses,
and, with a formidable company of warriors, set
out for Nine Pavilions. As soon as they had
entered the garden, they perceived Gulshad and
Shirzad conversing gaily together. Gulshad,
catching sight of them, became very uneasy,
whereupon Shirzad asked : ' What ails you, fair
princess, why do I behold you thus distressed ? '
' Alas,' she replied, ' my father has been informed
of your coming and has sent a company of horsemen
here. I doubt not that they have come to seize
you and carry you hence. Hasten, and I will lead
you to a secret hiding-place.' Shirzad, angered
at this proposal, replied : ' How can you counsel
thus ? Bring me weapons, but go yourself to
yonder pavilion and remain there in security.'
Gulshad thereupon gave him a suit of armour,
buckled it upon him, and then withdrew.

Shirzad, thus fully armed and prepared, saw
Almas standing in the garden while Katmas
approached to seize him. When Katmas came
close to Shirzad, the prince, who had a goblet of
wine in his hand, quietly finished drinking it,
without appearing to take any notice of Katmas.
That officer sprang at him, but the prince drew his
sword and cleft him in twain. He then advanced
on Almas, whom he dispatched in like manner.
The other horsemen, on seeing this, turned and fled
to inform the king, who, amazed at their report,
called his vizier, and, having collected an army of
a thousand fully armed men, rode at their head to
Nine Pavilions.

Gulshad, from the high terrace of her pavilion,
saw the company in the distance and warned

Shirzad that a numerous army was approaching
at a great speed, led by the king himself. She was
full of fear at their coming, but Shirzad comforted
her and said : ' O you that are beautiful as the
moon, be neither grieved nor disturbed : am I not
a match for all of these ? ' ' But ', she replied,
' how can you, who have only twenty or thirty
slaves at your command, prevail against a thousand
tried warriors ? ' ' Have no fear,' said Shirzad,
' but bid your slaves bring here all the arms and
weapons that are in the palace.' This she did,
bringing complete coats of mail and weapons, so
that everything was ready for battle when the
king arrived and marshalled his troops.   In the
garden of the palace was a fort, and Shirzad having
placed his men in this, a long and fierce fight ensued.

Meanwhile, when two days had passed and
Shirzad had not returned, Asad became very
uneasy, and decided at last to set out in search of
him with a strong force of armed men. They came
at length to Nine Pavilions, where the battle was
raging fiercely, and, falling upon the king's men,
soon put them to flight. Those who escaped fled
to the city, shut the gates and barricaded them.
Asad, after pursuing them for some space, returned
to Nine Pavilions, where he decided to remain, for
he found it very agreeable. Gulshad and Shirzad
came forward together to greet him, and bade him
bring his caravan to encamp there. The merchant
was greatly pleased with the princess, and from
his stores gave her many jewels and rich robes.

Bihzad, full of grief at his ill-success, retired to
his palace at Darband. His viziers and counsellors
and the nobles of his kingdom gathered round
him to console him and to offer their services.

Farsbahram, who was chief vizier, approached the
king and said : ' Your Majesty, grant me permission to go and speak with this fierce enemy.
I undertake so to beguile him, that I will make him
reasonable and bring him to submit to your
Majesty.' The King consented. Farsbahram,
therefore, came to Nine Pavilions and was admitted
to the presence of Asad, who at once recognized
him, though feigning ignorance. He remembered
the history of Shirzad's birth, and he knew from
it that Farsbahram had written the account of it.

The vizier saluted the merchant, and, greeting
him with many compliments, said : ' Merchants
are prudent and understanding men, for they have
travelled over the whole world. You must surely
know that your trading only prospers through the
protection and goodwill of kings, with whom
therefore it is not wise to quarrel. If you wish to
succeed in your present enterprise, summon your
son that we may all go together to pay our
respects to His Majesty, and to place your son at
his service ; you will then be able to obtain
everything that your heart desires.' Many other
things he said to persuade Asad, who then replied :
' Vizier, I have several questions to ask of you.
Firstly, do you know who this youth is ? ' ' Surely ',
replied the vizier, ' he is your son.' ' No,' said
Asad, ' he is the son of Karkin. It was he whose
mother, by the order of Bihzad, was sent into the
forest infested by lions. You arrived a few
moments after her death and saw the babe. Taking
pity on it, you wrote on a paper the details of all
that had occurred, then rolled up the paper and
made it fast with the necklace of jewels. Three
years later, having occasion to travel through the

forest, I found my way blocked by lions. On the back of one of them the child sat. We attacked them, and captured the lion upon which he was riding. I took the collar from his neck, read what was on the paper, and have reared him under the name of Shirzad.'

When he had finished his story, the merchant produced the jewelled collar. The vizier recognized it and threw himself at the feet of Shirzad in thankfulness for his preservation. Then, for the first time, Shirzad learned the story of his life. After its recital Farsbahram announced that he would go to Bihzad and inform him how matters stood, and would persuade him to give up the throne to Shirzad, who was the true heir.

As soon as Farsbahram's arrival at the palace was known, the king and the nobles gathered round him to hear his story. After recounting the history of Shirzad he added : ' This son of King Karkin to-day demands his throne and his crown, and swears to act nobly when they are given to him.' When the vizier had given his account of what had occurred, many of the servants of the old king, and all the nobles, withdrew from Bihzad, who at last went humbly to Nine Pavilions to ask pardon of Shirzad. He agreed to transfer to the rightful king his throne and his royal authority, and to submit to all his wishes. At the same time, the nobles who accompanied him acclaimed the marriage of Shirzad with Gulshad. The new king was carried to the capital, where he was given the keys of the city, of the forts, and of the treasure houses, and he had new coins struck, with his name upon them.

The royal couple spent the first day in the pavilion dedicated to the moon, and passed their time in joy and pleasure. Towards the end of the day, Shirzad said to the princess : ' You know that your father slew my mother, and I must therefore be revenged upon him.' Now, as may be imagined, Gulshad was anxious to deliver her father, so she consulted the stars concerning his destiny, and found that during the nine following days there would be a conjunction of the stars of evil influence against him, but that afterwards the position of the stars would change and be favourable. She therefore went to Shirzad and said to him : ' O Prince, may Allah prosper your life. I know that you have great power, but be advised that the pavilion in which we are now seated is devoted to the moon, and its influence is favourable to knaves and spies, as was proved by the case of the knave who carried off the king's daughter by trickery.'

This roused the prince's curiosity, and he said : ' Tell me what happened to her.' Whereupon Gulshad repeated to him the story of

AKHTAR THE CUT-PURSE

It is related that in Rum there was a king who had a daughter, Mahi Manzar, so beautiful that she delighted all who beheld her. One evening, at the close of a hot day, Mahi Manzar went upon the roof to breathe the cool air, and there she walked with her attendants. It happened that evening that on the roof of the bazaar near the palace, there was a youth named Akhtar, who gained his livelihood by knavery and roguery of every kind. He saw the princess on the roof, at his first glance was entranced by her beauty, and determined to carry her off. He remained on the roof of the bazaar all night, contriving a plan, and slept at home all the next day. When night fell he procured a long rope in which he tied a noose, and, making his way to the palace, stood at the base of the wall, at the place where he had last seen the princess.

He waited until it was very late, and when he saw that there were no more passers-by, he flung up his rope so that the noose was caught on one of the pinnacles on top of the wall. Very carefully and quietly he climbed up the rope and stepped on to the roof. There all was still, and he crept along until he came to a partition. He looked over this to see whether there was any one there, and to his dismay saw a sentry standing on guard. Akhtar crouched down in the shadow of the wall and lay concealed there, hoping that the sentry would fall asleep or go away, but as the first hour passed, and then a second and a third, the rogue decided to go home and try again the next night, having discovered at least that the princess's chamber lay in that direction. He went back to his rope, slid down it, unlooped it from the pinnacle by a strong upward jerk, and then went home to wait.

The next night he came again in the same fashion, but again failed. And so, night after night, he crept stealthily round the palace, scheming to find some way in, but for long he was unsuccessful.

There came a day when it was announced at the capital that Mihr Asar, Prince of Tabriz, was coming to ask the king for his daughter's hand in marriage. The news made Akhtar desperate, but fortune was soon to favour him. The arrival of the Prince of Tabriz was celebrated by a great feast, to which all the notables of the city were invited, and with great ceremony the prince and princess were betrothed. That night Akhtar took his rope again, and, throwing it up, climbed on to the parapet of the princess's chamber. The guards and sentries, as he had hoped, were all drunk with wine after the feast, and fast asleep. Clambering noiselessly down the steps into the courtyard of the palace, he made for the chamber where he knew the princess lay, and, creeping in, found her fast asleep. He held to her nose a powerful drug which assured that she should remain unconscious for some time, and then took her into his arms and carried her to the rope. He tied her to the end of it, climbed up himself, and, on reaching the roof, pulled her up after him. He then transferred the rope from the balcony to a pinnacle on the outer wall, let the princess gently down to the ground and climbed down after her. Once in the street he untied the rope, and, as fast as he could, made for the open country with his precious burden.

He had gone about ten miles from the town and had laid the girl down to rest, when she opened her eyes, and finding herself in thick darkness, cried out in alarm for her attendants. The only reply she received was from Akhtar, who greeted her and said : ' Have no fear.' She arose, finding herself in the open and with a strange man standing over her. ' Where am I ? ' she asked. Akhtar replied : ' O my dear one, I am Akhtar the Cut-purse. From the day when I saw you on the roof of the palace

I have loved you, and nearly died of longing for you. Now at last you have come into my possession, and I have carried you all night to this place. I pray you not to fear, and to count me your slave.'

The princess was utterly overwhelmed by this, but at last thought to herself: 'As he has carried me off by knavery, I must think of some stratagem which will enable me to escape from him.' So she replied: 'On the very day that you saw me, I saw you, and my heart desired you, but there has been no chance of meeting you. Now however that we have met, we cannot remain here amongst these mountains and caves. Let us go to some town and find a house in which to live.'

When Akhtar had approved of her suggestion the princess said: 'But I cannot travel along the road as I am, dressed as a woman. I must have man's clothes, to prevent trouble on the way.' The cut-purse again agreed. He tied Mahi Manzar's hair into plaits and concealed it under a kerchief. Then he drew a man's cloak around her and they set out, taking the road to Aleppo.

For nearly a month they were on the way, and at last arrived at the outskirts of the town, where there was a caravanserai. The first night they stayed there and entered into conversation with an old man and his wife, who lived in the place. In the morning the princess said to Akhtar: 'The journey has made me feel faint. I will ask this old woman to make me some soup.' 'I will go to the town at once,' said he, 'and bring something good to eat.' He thereupon departed, and arrived at Aleppo just as the gates were opening.

Now it happened that during the night an assassin had made an attack on the king of Aleppo and seriously wounded him. The royal guard and servants were therefore searching everywhere for the culprit, and they arrested every suspicious person whom they saw, in the hope of finding him. As soon as they saw Akhtar, who was dressed as a foreigner, they pounced upon him, and asked him to give an account of himself. They were not satisfied by his answers and were continuing to question him, when a Rumi, who had known Akhtar in Rum, came up and said : ' I know him. He is Akhtar, a great rogue.' The cut-purse was therefore taken away and thrown into prison.

Two days later the king felt that his sickness was grievous and that he had no hope of life. His kinsfolk were summoned, and to them he spoke his last wishes. ' I am dying,' said he, ' and have no son to follow me. When I am dead, wait three days, and then go out early on the morrow, gather all the people together, and let loose my Arab greyhound. The first person whom it catches by the skirt is to be made king after me.'

The next day the king died, and for the three following days the city was in mourning. At dawn on the fourth day criers were sent out, and the whole populace gathered outside the city. An Arab greyhound was carried out, and the announcement was made that the first person whose clothes it caught after it was released should be made king.

Amongst the crowd that gathered round the crier was the princess Mahi Manzar, still dressed as a man. When Akhtar had left her she had waited a little while, and then set out for the city ; but, seeing the crowd emerging, she had gone with it to see what was happening.

By some strange chance, as soon as the grey-hound was released, it made straight for Mahi Manzar and caught hold of her robe. The crowd, seeing an exceedingly handsome youth, carried Mahi Manzar off, according to the king's will, and set her upon the throne and made her king, thinking that she was a man.

Now though she was but a girl, Mahi Manzar was a king's daughter and knew the ways of kingship and the value of justice and equity. Her first act was to command that throughout her kingdom all prisoners should be released, and in many other ways she set herself to gain the favour of her subjects, freeing them also from taxation for one year.

Amongst those released from prison was Akhtar, who at once made his way to the caravanserai. Not finding the princess, he questioned the old man and woman about her, and they told him that she had left soon after him, and gone to the town. In despair, Akhtar, who had for safety's sake disguised himself as a dervish, sought everywhere in the neighbourhood, but found no trace of the princess.

But he was not alone in his search. On the morning after the princess's disappearance from home, her parents and companions were filled with alarm when they could not find her. They made inquiries everywhere and discovered that Akhtar, the knave and cut-purse, had also left the city. It occurred to them that he might be responsible for Mahi Manzar's disappearance, and so they began to search for him. Prince Mihr Asar, to whom the maiden was betrothed, took it upon himself to direct the search, saying that it most concerned him. With a hundred servants he left

the city and cast about for traces of the culprit.
After several days they came within a short
distance of Aleppo, and while looking about for
clues, they started a gazelle. Mihr Asar at once
went in pursuit, and followed it two or three leagues.
The gazelle tired at last, and the prince, loosing off
an arrow, shot it dead. He dismounted, picked up
the gazelle, and went on his way. As he proceeded,
he saw, seated under a tree, a man dressed as
a dervish; so he again dismounted, greeted him,
and sat down. Having entered into conversation,
they lit a fire of wood and roasted the gazelle.
When they had eaten, the prince lay down to rest
putting his weapons under his head, and was soon
asleep.

When Akhtar, for it was no other, saw that he
had the prince at his mercy, he leaped upon him,
bound him so that he could not move, and, taking
his cloak and weapons, seated himself upon the
prince's horse and rode off. Unluckily for him,
however, Mihr Asar's servants were then coming up
in search of their master, and seeing the dervish
upon the prince's horse, they seized him, bound
his hands together, and tied a rope around his neck.
The rogue then confessed to them that he had
stolen the horse, and that they would find the
prince bound under a certain tree. At this they
galloped on, taking Akhtar with them, and soon
had the prince free and told their story.

Driving the cut-purse in front of them with the
rope round his neck, they reached Aleppo and made
their way to the king's palace. There the prince
informed the vizier that he was a stranger to the
city, that his betrothed had disappeared, and that
he was searching for her. The vizier reported this

to his sovereign, who ordered that a handsome
lodging was to be given to Mihr Asar, and every
attention shown him.

That day Mahi Manzar arranged a court to which
the prince was summoned. There he told the whole
of his story; how he had come to Tabriz and had
been betrothed to the king's daughter, how she
had disappeared and he had gone in search of her,
had met Akhtar the cut-purse, and arrived at last
at Aleppo.

After hearing the prince's adventures Mahi
Manzar ordered Akhtar to be brought in and commanded him to give an account of himself. 'Tell
me the entire truth,' said she, 'or else I will have
you hanged.' The rogue in his turn recounted his
doings from the time of having seen the princess,
and confessed all, without concealing anything.
Mahi Manzar then revealed herself, and ordered
Akhtar to be led away. Then, with the least
possible delay, she celebrated her marriage to the
prince, whom she made king of Aleppo. And so
farewell to them.

Shirzad was much pleased by Gulshad's story;
the execution of Bihzad was put off for that day,
and the newly-wedded pair spent the remainder
of it in feasting and merrymaking. On the second
day they repaired to the pavilion of Utarid, which
is Mercury, and there resumed the feast. But as
he sat drinking wine, the wrong done to his mother
came to the mind of Shirzad, and he gave orders
that Bihzad was to be thrown from the roof of the
pavilion in which they were. Gulshad was distracted by news of this, and coming to the king,
sat down by his side.

Shirzad caressed her, saying : ' Do not let your heart be grieved. I must have vengeance upon your father for my mother's death, for you know that the law demands retribution.'

She replied : ' May the king's life and that of the empire be long. It is known that everything which occurs is pre-ordained by fate, and the influence of the heavens regulates all below them. This pavilion in which we are now seated is devoted to Mercury, which is the protector of poets, writers, and soothsayers. The proof lies in the story of the necromancer who was born under the ascendancy of this star.'

Shirzad asked what that was, and the queen proceeded to narrate

THE STORY OF AFZAL THE SOOTHSAYER

It is recorded that in the city of Balkh there was once a soothsayer, Afzal, who was also a skilled magician. In soothsaying he was the foremost of his time, and by his art everything was revealed to him. He spent his whole time in the service of the king, who consulted him on all matters, and who thereby knew and understood all that was happening.

One day the king from his private apartments sent for the magician, and told him to cast about and reveal what the day would bring forth. It chanced that the king's daughter, Mihr Anduz, a maiden of surpassing beauty, entered the apartment and saw Afzal there, working with the sand which he used and making divinations and forecasts. When he had finished she approached him, holding concealed in her hand a golden orange, and said: 'Cast about in the grains and divine what it is that I have in my hand.' Afzal, reading the message, said : ' It is a golden orange.'

Now the soothsayer was greatly in love with the princess, and when she gave him the golden orange as a reward for his skill, he was delighted beyond measure ; and when she asked him to teach her the art of sand-reading, he consented with great goodwill. Day after day, therefore, Afzal came to instruct the princess in magic. By the time she had learned sufficient of the art, and before Afzal left the king's service, Mihr Anduz had discovered by the magician's words and actions that he was in love with her. Although he now saw her no more, he kept his love, and when at last he realized that he could not succeed in his aim of winning her, he lost his reason, and wandered distracted through the town.

News of Afzal's madness was brought to the king, who ordered that he was to be taken to a wizard, who might treat him. So the magician was taken away, and after long treatment was cured of his madness, but his love remained, and indeed had greatly increased. At last he thought to himself that, in his present form, he could never hope to marry the princess, and so he devised a stratagem.

He had a son, whom on his arrival home he summoned, and said : ' I have a secret to reveal to you and a task which I wish you to perform. Out of it you will derive great benefit, and I too will thereby attain my desire. But you must guard the secret.' The youth agreed to do everything his father wished, and the latter then said : ' I am going to turn myself by magic into a parrot. When I am in that form, put me into a cage and announce that your father has suddenly died. Then procure a coffin and bury it, and pretend to be in mourning, as the custom is, for the next forty days. At the end of that period take the parrot to the king, and say : " This is a talking parrot to which my father taught the art of sooth-saying ; he can cast about in sand, and declare all that is to happen. Now, since my father has died, I have brought the bird to be the king's servant." Then hand me in the cage to the king, and he will certainly reward you handsomely.'

The youth carried out all that he was told : when the magician had transformed himself, he put the parrot into a cage, and two days later told his friends that his father had died. A coffin was prepared, and he himself closed it up. After the funeral he observed his forty days of mourning and received many condolences from the king and all the inhabitants of Balkh, who greatly regretted the loss of the soothsayer. When the forty days of mourning ceremonies were at an end, the sooth-sayer's son came to the king, bringing the parrot in a cage, and, presenting it, said : ' This parrot was left by my father. It is a soothsayer, and I have brought it that it may be of service to your Majesty, for by means of its art it can reveal all that is hidden.'

The king set the parrot down in front of him and spoke to it, and the bird fittingly replied. Then, concealing something in his hand, the king said : ' Divine what it is that I have in my hand.' The bird from his cage asked for a board, and throwing sand upon it traced out what the king had taken in his hand. This pleased the monarch greatly, and he gave the soothsayer's son a rich present and released him from payment of taxation, so that he returned home a wealthy man and became a person of importance. When he had gone, the king took the parrot to his daughter and said: 'Afzal has died and has left this parrot; it is a soothsayer, and can declare all that is happening.' The princess in her turn tried the parrot, and was delighted to receive a correct reply. She kept the bird by her constantly and took it into her sleeping chamber. In the night the magician broke out of the cage, turned into his ordinary form, and going up to the sleeping princess kissed her, then, seeing that she was about to wake, changed himself back again and returned to the cage.

The princess on waking looked round, but could see no one, and went to sleep again. In the morning she told her sister what had happened, and both were puzzled at the mystery; nevertheless they decided to tell no one. The next night and the next the parrot broke out of the cage and kissed the princess, each time returning before she could see him. At last she put the parrot before her and said: 'I wish you to cast about in the sand and tell me what you see there. Hide nothing from me and tell me the truth.'

The parrot of course knew what troubled her, and casting about in the sand said: 'The son of the king of the Peris is in love with you, and has several times come and embraced you.' 'I bid you tell this to no one,' said the maiden; and the parrot promised to keep the secret.

The next night the princess remained awake but lay very still. Hearing a sound she looked round in the direction from whence it came, and saw the parrot come out of the cage and suddenly appear as a handsome young man, superbly dressed. In alarm she cried out : ' Who are you ? ' and he answered : ' I am the son of the king of the Peris. I have loved you now for three years and have never yet succeeded in my desire to declare my love for you ; so I transformed myself into a sooth-saying parrot and came here to fulfil my wish. Now I have changed back to my own form.'

The princess at once fell in love with the comely youth standing before her in the moonlight. They talked for many hours and arranged that he should live near her as a bird in his cage, and only resume his own form when no one was about.

Some time later, the king of Merv conceived the idea of asking for Mihr Anduz as a wife for his son, and he sent his vizier with a rich present to Balkh. On reaching the outskirts of Balkh the vizier sent a message to announce to the king of Balkh that the vizier of the king of Merv was approaching. The monarch ordered that he was to be received with all due honour, and the next day the vizier was brought before him and presented his master's gift and a letter. When he had read the letter the king said : ' There has always been friendship between us, and now this will be a fresh sign of our goodwill ; therefore I gladly consent.'

When the king returned to his own apartment, he told the queen what had occurred. Mihr Anduz soon heard news of it too, and was greatly troubled, for it portended much humiliation for her. So she turned to the parrot for help and asked what she was to do. The parrot replied : ' Do not grieve, and set your mind at rest. You must leave the palace with the vizier, only, when you go, take me with you, and leave all else to me.' So the princess was consoled.

Some time later, when all the necessary preparations for the wedding had been made, the princess set out with the vizier for Merv, and the king came out to welcome her and to escort her to the palace. For a whole week the city was decorated and its inhabitants feasted, and with great pomp Mihr Anduz was married to the prince Farrukh Ruz. Immediately after the wedding, the parrot, by his power of wizardry, threw the prince into a trance, so that he lay as one dead. The whole of the court was greatly dismayed at this, for all the art of the physicians was of no avail. At last, after ten days of ceaseless effort, the queen remembered that not far from the city there lived a sorceress, whose advice she sought. The sorceress heard the story, and undertook to come and set the matter right. So all together returned to the prince's palace to effect the cure. While they were resting from their journey, the sorceress saw the parrot, and at once recognizing that it was a magic bird, she rose and left the house, accompanied by the vizier. To him she said : ' All the trouble has been caused by that parrot. I will transform myself into a cat. You go into the house, call the parrot to you and make it divine by means of sand. Keep it occupied until I come in, so that I can bite off its head and kill it. Its magic will then be entirely undone, and the prince will recover.' The vizier did as he was bid, so that the bird was employed in divining while the cat entered quietly from behind. In a moment the animal had pounced upon the parrot and killed it. As it died, the bird-like form disappeared, giving place to the lifeless body of a man, while the prince at once awoke from his trance.

As soon as she saw this, the princess realized how she had been deceived by Afzal, and she commanded that the body be taken out and buried and that the wedding celebrations should be resumed.

When Gulshad had told the story, Shirzad, in his pleasure at it, forgot the punishment of Bihzad; and on the third day they took up their abode in the pavilion of Zuhra, which is Venus, and were sitting joyously feasting, when Shirzad remembered again his plan of avenging his mother. Once more he summoned his servants and told them to bring Bihzad and cast him from the roof of the pavilion. Gulshad heard the order given, and seating herself by the king's side, she said: 'Your majesty, the pavilion in which we are now seated is under the protection of Venus, and is devoted to love and pleasure. No injustice or bloodshed can be wrought here. The pavilion is made for the harp and the lute and the rebeck, as is proved by the story of the harpist over whom Venus exercised her influence.' 'What was that?' asked Shirzad, and the princess began the story of

NAHID AND HER HARP

It is related that in the town of Kirman there was a girl, Nahid, who played upon the harp. Her beauty was superb and her skill in playing excelled all in her day. She had two attendants, both good to look upon, one Mihr and the other Mushtari, one of whom played the lute and the other the harp. Now although Nahid was not married, she had many suitors, for the fame of her beauty and of her talents had spread abroad in the world, so that when she played or sang, crowds of merry-makers gathered round her.

One day the king of the peris, being about to celebrate his wedding, prepared a great feast, and decided to have human minstrels at the festivities, which were to last for several days. The fame of Nahid having reached him, he summoned one of his peris, and said: ' Go to Kirman and bring me Nahid.' The peri at once appeared in Kirman, and went to Nahid's house. There he found the musicians singing and playing before a great company in the courtyard; so, changing himself into a nightingale, he perched on the branch of a tree. When Nahid began to sing, the nightingale too burst into song and followed Nahid note by note, until all the company were amazed at the sweetness of the bird's melody. While they all stood gazing at it, the nightingale flew down from its branch, snatched up Nahid and her harp, bore her aloft, and disappeared. The people cried aloud in dismay at the sight, and scattering in all directions searched for Nahid, but in vain.

Meanwhile Nahid was carried to the abode of the peris, and set down in the midst of their assembly. All around her in the apartment, she heard voices, but was alarmed to find that she could see none of the speakers. As she stood there, one of the peris approached, and rubbed upon her eyes some of Solomon's collyrium, which enables mortals to see treasures in the earth. Immediately, she beheld the whole assembly of peris, in the midst of whom was a throne of gold, and, seated upon it, she saw

a maiden, radiant as the sun, who rejoiced at the
scene of revelry, for all the peris were singing and
laughing.

Nahid felt exceedingly ill-at-ease and strange
in this company, and scarcely knew what to do.
Meantime, the peri who had carried her off
brought her harp to her, but she was distraught
by her fears, and paid no attention to it. Seeing
her thus, the peri maiden who was seated upon the
throne summoned Nahid to her and tried to soothe
her. 'We only desire you to be here with us during
our festal days,' she said. 'After that we will take
you whithersoever you desire.' The harpist was
reassured at this, and taking her harp, she began
to play, so that her music delighted the peris, who
acclaimed her loudly. For three days of feasting she
remained there, singing and playing, and then
turning to the maiden on the throne, she said:
'Now that the feast is at an end, let me return to
my own home. My friends have no news of where
I am or of what has become of me. They do not
know whether I am dead or living.' The peri
replied kindly, and thus reassured, Nahid asked
that she might take with her from the land of
the peris something unknown amongst mortals,
and so be able to give a token of the place where
she had been.

At this the peri summoned one of her attendants
and commanded that a certain casket be brought.
This she opened and showed Nahid four fruits that
lay inside. 'These fruits', said she, 'are such
that if a man and woman each eat of them, the man
becomes a woman and the woman a man. Then,
if they eat the remaining fruits, they will regain
their original forms.' She then gave the four fruits

with the casket to Nahid, put a rich robe on her shoulders, and handed her over to the charge of the same peri who had brought her.

Nahid returned to her own house at Kirman in the twinkling of an eye, and when she entered the house she found her companions and friends in mourning for her; since, having sought for her for several days after her disappearance and having found no trace of her, they had assumed that she was dead. They were astonished as they sat there, to see Nahid appear as if from nowhere, laden with a great array of treasures. Filled with joy at her return, they greeted her and danced round her in welcome.

The story of Nahid's adventure soon spread over the whole world. It became known how the peris had carried her off, how she had sung and played at the peri king's wedding, and how she had returned laden with gifts. Before long the story reached Ispahan, Persia's capital, and the talk was of nothing but Nahid and her playing and singing.

Now the Shah of Ispahan had a son, Jamshid, who spent all his time in pleasure, and who sought the acquaintance of every beautiful woman in the land. The fame of Nahid awoke in him the desire to meet her, and at last, taking a large sum of gold from his father's treasury, he set out for Kirman with twenty servants. After travelling for some time he arrived at his destination, sought out a lodging, and when he had settled his household, accompanied by a servant he made his way to Nahid's house. A slave announced that Jamshid, son of the Shah of Ispahan, had come on a visit, and Nahid ordered that he was to be admitted.

When he entered, she greeted him with the utmost graciousness, and Jamshid, delighted with her beauty and charm, there and then fell in love with her. While they conversed a great feast was prepared, and soon they sat down to eat and drink. Cup-bearers of surpassing loveliness handed round ruby red wine, and in music and feasting they passed the whole day.

Early the next morning the prince again visited Nahid, bringing with him Ispahan robes of cloth of gold, and jewels. Again they feasted, and when night came Jamshid departed, more enraptured than ever, but having as yet found no opportunity of declaring his love. For ten days this continued; then at last Nahid said to him : ' I know, Prince, that your heart inclines towards me, and by your conduct you have shown that you love me. If we can be married with your father's goodwill, then I will consent to go with you.'

These words delighted the prince beyond measure, and summoning the *khatib*, he was wedded to the harpist. All that day there was drinking of wine and feasting and rejoicing. In the midst of the merriment Nahid remembered the four fruits in the casket, and decided in jest to try them. Squeezing the juice of one into a goblet, she gave it to her husband to drink, but she did not tell him what it was ; then she drank the juice of another. Immediately their outward form was changed, Nahid assumed the body and garments of Jamshid and the prince those of Nahid. Jamshid was not only frightened but enraged at the change, and at last when he found that he still remained outwardly a woman, he fell into a deep despondency though Nahid did her best to comfort him. So they lived for about a year: then, one day, there came a letter from Ispahan saying that the king, Jamshid's father, had died, leaving his throne and kingdom to his son, and that the prince must return to Ispahan without delay. Jamshid was deeply distressed at the news, but decided eventually that he must go and claim his throne, even if it were in his present guise. Now Nahid had a secret desire to be ruler of Ispahan herself, and so consented eagerly to go with her husband. After the necessary preparations they set out, and all the way Jamshid pondered how he was to explain his present womanly form. Day and night his thoughts were of nothing but this, and he prayed to be restored to his former self. One night in a dream he saw a peri who approached him and told him of a certain place where a casket was concealed. ' Take it and open it,' she said, ' and you will find two fruits. Squeeze each into a goblet ; then when you are about to retire to sleep, drink one cup yourself and make Nahid drink the other, and each of you will be as you were before.'

When Jamshid awoke he was filled with new hope. Secretly he sought out the casket, and taking the fruits, squeezed the juice out of them. That night, when Nahid was asleep, he drank the juice of one fruit, and at once was a man again in form and strength, and then, going quietly to his wife, he forced open her mouth, and poured the juice down her throat. Immediately Nahid awoke, again a beautiful woman. She was surprised and greatly disappointed at what had happened, and demanded to know what Jamshid had done. The prince explained his dream and how he had found the fruits; whereupon Nahid confessed how she had first brought about the transformation and asked for forgiveness. The prince was so pleased to be himself again, that he forgot to be angry, and soon afterwards they reached Ispahan, where they lived together as king and queen in great prosperity.

When Gulshad had finished her story, Shirzad, who had been much amused and pleased at it, commanded that a feast should be prepared, then again in feasting and revelry the punishment of Bihzad was forgotten. The next day they went to the fourth pavilion, which was dedicated to the sun, and there feasted again.

When Shirzad had drunk his fill of wine he remembered the matter of his mother and Bihzad, and sent a slave to bring the vizier and avenge his mother's death. Gulshad then came and sat down by the prince's side. ' O prince,' said she, ' to-day we are in the pavilion of the sun, whose influence works in strange ways, as in the matter of the king of Nishapur and his wonderful adventure.'

' What was that ? ' asked the prince, ' and how was the king released from the sun's influence ? ' Thereupon Gulshad began the story of

KHURSHID AND THE WHITE GENIE

It is related that at Nishapur there once lived a king named Khurshid, who was beloved by all his subjects. He was young and generous and delighted in justice. One day whilst out hunting he saw an enormous boar, and at once set off in pursuit, shouting out to his attendants to follow him. The boar leapt in and out among the trees with the king hard upon its track, but he never came near enough to spear it. The followers one after another dropped behind with weariness, but Khurshid still kept on, until at last he too was compelled to dismount in order to rest his horse. By that time the animal had escaped into the distance, and the king, finding himself upon a lonely mountain-side, determined to turn back. He soon found, however, that he had utterly lost his way, and so decided, since it was rapidly getting dark, to spend the night beside the first stream that he saw, and there rest both his horse and himself.

With the dawn, Khurshid mounted his horse and began to climb the mountain, in the hope that when he reached the top he could discover where he was, and so choose the best road home. But as he made his way up, he suddenly came upon a white marble reservoir set in the earth, with a marble bench carved out of the same piece of stone set by the brink. The king, much amazed, advanced and looked into the water. It was clear as crystal, but so deep that the bottom could not be seen. Thinking to try the depth of it, the king picked up a stone and threw it in. Instantly there was a piercing shriek, and the king felt himself seized and dragged down and down through the water. So swift was the motion that he lost his breath, and finally became unconscious. When he came to himself, he found that he was in a great hall of white marble, so lofty that the roof could not be seen. On a throne before him he saw a white genie, who looked at him savagely and asked : ' Who are you, and what do you here ? Do you not know that this is my home, and I forbid the presence of any human ? ' Khurshid answered in alarm that he had been hunting and lost his way. When he had finished speaking, the genie said : ' You need not fear death here, if you agree to one condition. I never yet felt what it is like to be a king on earth, and I wish to try. Give me your clothes, and I will go to Nishapur to reign in your stead. You will stay here to guard my treasures.'

The unfortunate Khurshid stripped off his clothes and handed them over to the genie, who put them on, and, modelling his features to resemble the king's, vanished out of his sight.

For a long time Khurshid remained where he was, sunk in deep grief at his misfortune. But after several hours he began to feel very hungry, so set out in search of food. All around the great hall were numerous doors, and he stood uncertain, not knowing which to try first. Going at last to the one straight before him, he opened it, and found himself in a large apartment in which a sumptuous meal was all ready set out. Khurshid approached, and seating himself, ate ravenously, finding each dish more delicious than the last. When he had satisfied his hunger he looked for something to drink, but he saw neither water, milk, nor wine. In one corner of the room, almost concealed by a thick hanging, was a tiny door. Going to it, Khurshid opened it, and saw that it led into a long corridor, draped with tapestries and with a magnificent crimson carpet running its whole length. He stepped in, and for many minutes walked along it, looking for some other door. At last, set in a corner at the very end, he found one, and, passing through it, entered a beautiful domed chamber. In the midst of it was a throne, and lying upon it was a golden crown which the white genie had left there.

The king, amazed at the splendour of all he saw, walked round the chamber to admire the flashing gems set in the walls. On his way round he came to another door, and, impelled by his thirst, opened this and found himself in a long vaulted gallery made of white crystal. Along this he walked for the greater part of an hour, almost overcome by thirst. In the distance he saw yet another door and ran hard towards it. It opened of its own accord at his approach and he passed through into a superb garden. On all sides were fruit trees laden with the most delicious fruits, and little streams of clear water ran in all directions over beds of jewels. Khurshid threw himself down and drank his fill and rested. Then he rose and walked about in this enchanting spot, picking the fruit from the trees and eating it as he went. Night came at last and he lay down under a tree, and being very weary, soon fell into a deep sleep.

When day dawned, Khurshid awoke and spent a long time bathing leisurely in the stream and making his breakfast on the many fruits that he saw. As he walked slowly along, a great palace came into view, and towards this he made his way. On approaching he saw that it was built of white marble, and that for windows it had emeralds and rubies of enormous size. He entered, to find himself in a magnificently hung chamber in which stood a couch, and upon it sat a ravishing damsel. She did not move at his entry, and he was amazed at this until he observed that she was bound hand and foot. At his greeting she replied pleasantly and invited him to be seated and to tell her how he had come there. 'Do you not know', said she, 'that this is the abode of the white genie, and that entry is forbidden to the children of men ? '

The king in reply recounted his adventure from beginning to end, and then turning to the damsel he asked : ' But how is it that you are here, why are you bound, and who are you ? ' ' I am ', she replied, ' the daughter of the king of the genii, and in our own kingdom I was famed for my beauty. One day, when I was walking in my father's garden, the white genie suddenly appeared, carried me off, and brought me here, where he keeps me bound and powerless to escape. He gives me everything that is necessary to life, and indeed I am surrounded by every luxury, but I am entirely alone here and for months I have not spoken to any one, so that I am saddened and miserable. But your arrival fills me with hope. I flatter myself that you will stay here at least a little while in my company, so that we may talk of escape.'

Dazzled by her beauty, Khurshid promised to remain as long as she wished, and not to rest until he had found the means of rescuing both her and himself. ' I am sad ', said he, ' to think who we are, and how far we are separated from our homes and our friends. But I do not know what our destiny is, whether there is any hope at all of our escape from this place, or whether we are condemned to stay here for ever.' ' There is one means,' replied the princess, ' which I have been afraid to try alone, but which, now that you are here, may lead us both to safety. Near here is a gallery which runs far underground. It is utterly dark and black, and no ray of light penetrates there. At the end of it there is a round chamber where, in the very centre, hangs a mirror. Upon this mirror there is

inscribed in magic characters the spell which keeps
us both here, and which, if read, reveals the secret
of the power of the white genie. Once you have
the glass in your hand, you must look into it edge-
wise, and then you will be able to read what is
written on it. Also, if you look through it in this
way, the genie will at once resume his old form
and will fall into your power so that you can kill
him. But, to succeed, you must have the mirror
always in your hand when you deal with him.'

The king was delighted at this, and asked her to
tell him at once where the mouth of the underground passage was. She described it carefully,
and Khurshid at once departed. In the wall
immediately behind the couch was fixed a large
green stone. On Khurshid's pressing it, it moved
round, as the princess had said, and he found
himself plunged into thick darkness. Slowly and
carefully, not knowing what to expect, he made
his way for hours along it. At last, seeing a tiny
spot of light in the air, he knew that he was in the
round chamber, and that the mirror was shining at
him. With a great leap he seized and plucked it
down, and then, as quickly as possible, made his
way back to the princess's chamber and the light.
There he saw that on its face were written magic
symbols, and, holding it sideways, he found that
he could read them. He called them out aloud and
immediately the bonds fell from the princess, and
she was free to walk and move about.

Together they left the palace and the garden,
going back by the same way that Khurshid had
come. They soon reached the dwelling of the white
genie, and there rested for a short time. Then the
princess of the genii took the king by the hand

and pulled him after her out of the reservoir. Once on land again the princess led the way to Nishapur.

When they reached the outskirts of the city, Khurshid decided to leave his companion outside for a time while he entered. 'There', he said, 'I will see my people, find out how matters stand, and obtain news of the genie. I can then make my plans accordingly, and will return for you here.' The princess agreed to this proposal, and Khurshid departed. He entered the town and made straight for the house of his vizier. There he said to the servants : 'Go to your master and tell him that a stranger has arrived with news which will rejoice him, and that he wishes to speak with him.'

One of the servants soon came back with the message that the vizier would see him, and ushered Khurshid into his master's presence. The king having saluted the vizier, who replied without showing any signs of recognition, asked him who he was and what matter brought him there. Khurshid could not restrain himself at this, and cried out, 'Vizier, do you not know me ? And have you forgotten me so soon ?'

The vizier was astonished at this, but what he had heard set his mind working. He remembered that ever since the person, whom all had taken to be Khurshid, had returned from the hunting expedition, he had been strange in his manner. He appeared to have forgotten in a moment all the business of the state. He scarcely knew his ministers, and utterly forgot to acknowledge and recognize his own favourite slave. 'Perhaps', thought the vizier, as he looked at Khurshid, 'this

is really our king Khurshid, and the other some
usurper.' 'Tell me then how it is that you are not
on the throne,' said he. 'Surely you must be mad
to speak so, when we know that the king is at this
very moment in his palace ?' Khurshid then told
him his adventures : 'He that now sits on the
throne is a white genie, who has usurped my
appearance by magic. He seized my clothes and
came here, while he kept me imprisoned in his
own abode, until I found a way to escape.' By
means of the mirror Khurshid then resumed his
own appearance before the eyes of the astonished
vizier, who thereupon approached him, and,
kneeling before him, asked for forgiveness, and
assured the king of his loyalty.

The next day the vizier summoned all the great
nobles of the capital and informed them of what
had occurred. They were all rejoiced to see the
real king again and proceeded in a body to the
palace, and to the chamber of the white genie.
As soon as Khurshid caught sight of him, he
turned the mirror sideways upon him. The genie
immediately resumed his ordinary form, and the
nobles fell upon him with their swords and hacked
him to pieces.

When this was over, the king returned to the
forest to find the princess. Together they returned
to the city, and the king, having asked her hand in
marriage, their wedding was celebrated with great
pomp and rejoicing.

When Gulshad finished her story, King Shirzad
was greatly pleased with it. He had red wine
brought in and offered to all, and while he feasted,
again forgot his desire to slay Bihzad.

On the fifth day the party moved to the pavilion of Mirrikh, which is Mars, where they continued their feasting. Then, in the midst of the merry-making, Shirzad remembered his promise of vengeance. Summoning his servants, he commanded them to bring in the vizier. Just as they were about to depart, Gulshad said : ' Your Majesty, this pavilion is sacred to Mirrikh, whose influence makes for the shedding of blood ; but by strange adventure one may sometimes avert this, as is seen in the strange case of the butcher. That was an amusing history.' ' What was it ? ' asked the king, and Gulshad proceeded to tell the story of

NASIR, THE BUTCHER

It is related that in the province of Turkistan there was once a city called Amad Khan, in which lived a youth, by trade a butcher, whose name was Nasir. He was a man of most handsome face and bearing, and his reputation for beauty had spread over the whole province. One day, he went out of the town with some of his companions to buy sheep. On the completion of their business they set out to return to the town again, but night fell before they arrived, so that they were compelled to camp in the fields to await the morning. In the middle of the night, two wolves descended on the flock, and each carried off a sheep. Nasir and his companions, being awakened by the bleating, went off in pursuit of their property. It was a very dark night, so that the party was soon scattered, and the butcher himself, wandering far out of his way, was utterly lost by the time morning came. Neither the wolves nor the town were anywhere in

sight, and at last Nasir resolved to abandon his
search and return home. But he had wandered
farther than he had imagined. For three days he
walked, and at last came upon a town which, to
his amazement, he saw was strange to him. He
entered, and walked about the streets and bazaars
looking for a butcher's shop, where he could find
help and counsel. At last he came to a shop where
he saw a handsome youth engaged in his business
of cutting up meat. Nasir approached and saluted
him, and the other youth, seeing a good-looking
man of about his own age, returned the greeting
pleasantly. After some conversation, Mansur—
for that was the shopman's name—invited Nasir
to be seated, and when his business was done
took him to his own home. In course of time
strong friendship grew up between the two, and
Nasir decided to remain where he was. Mansur
took him into partnership, and they shared alike
the labour and the profits of their trade.

One day there came to their shop a servant of
the king's vizier, to ask for some one to go to his
house and kill two or three sheep. Mansur sent
Nasir, who went to the house and killed and
dressed the sheep. While he was engaged in the
process of dressing the meat, the vizier's daughter,
Nasrat, who was herself beautiful as the moon,
espied him from the roof of a lodge in the vizier's
garden. She saw that he was very handsome, and,
as she watched him, with a thousand hearts she fell
in love with him. She looked so hard at him, that
at last Nasir's gaze was drawn upwards to the roof
of the lodge, and at his first glance the young
butcher became entranced with her beauty. From
time to time as he worked he gazed upwards

towards the maiden, and as far as possible pro-
longed his work. But the time came when no
further excuse remained for him to linger. He was
about to depart, when the vizier's daughter, who
had no wish to see him go, summoned the cook and
told him to keep the butcher till the meat was
cooked, and to let him have his dinner in the
kitchen before he went. On his return the cook
told Nasir that he was to wait till the meat was
cooked, and that he could go after he had dined.
Nasir thanked him and waited, and then after his
meal he departed, much to the grief of the vizier's
daughter, who saw him go. Nasir, returning to his
companion, explained to him why he had been
away so long, but he kept secret the matter of his
love.

The next day the vizier's daughter called the
cook's wife and, giving her a purse of gold, confessed her secret to her. ' I am in love ', said she,
' with that butcher. I saw him yesterday looking
towards me, and I know that he too is in love with
me. I want you to have him brought here every
day to kill sheep.' She ended by making the cook's
wife swear an oath not to reveal the secret to any
one.

Nasir, therefore, was summoned every day to
the vizier's house to kill sheep, and, while he was
performing his task, the maiden and he glanced
towards each other from afar, and longed to meet.
Nasrat at last could restrain herself no longer,
and one day said to the cook's wife, ' In some
manner arrange for us to meet.' The woman
consented and told Nasir what had occurred. He
replied, ' I am her servant and slave. What does
a blind man desire more than a seeing eye ? '

After some little while, when the vizier was away from home, the woman seized her opportunity, and, arranging a private place in her house, led Nasir there, and then brought the vizier's daughter. For an hour they sat there, Nasir telling his story and the maiden hers. Before she departed the vizier's daughter said, 'We must devise a plan whereby we can come together.' Nasir replied, 'I am your slave, and I will follow any sign you make.' 'Then,' said she, 'the best plan will be for you to carry me off from here and take me to your own town.' After much discussion they arranged that one night Nasir was to come to the wall of the vizier's palace, the girl would let down a rope from the roof, and then, when she had climbed down, she and Nasir were to leave the town together.

Very secretly they made their plans for departure, and decided on a particular night. Finally they took the cook's wife into their confidence, for they could not succeed without her help, and the vizier's daughter gave Nasir two big purses full of money to buy what was necessary.

On the appointed night, after the first watch of the night had passed, the young butcher made his way to the wall of the vizier's palace and sat down under it at the appointed place to wait. He had been hard at work all day, and the night was warm, so that soon he nodded with sleep, but he roused himself again. Gradually, however, sleep overcame him and, all unconscious, he lay down where he was.

It happened at that time that a gang of robbers was working in the city. They numbered about ten, the chief of the gang being a cut-throat named

Sām, and their method was to go about thieving separately, but to share all profits. That night one of them, named Kihtar, had gone towards the vizier's palace with the object of breaking in. As he walked under the wall looking for a means of entry, he saw a person on the flat roof letting down a rope, and at once imagined that it was another robber. Quickly he concealed himself in an angle of the wall, intending to spring upon the other by surprise and take away any booty he had.

Thus it was that when the vizier's daughter climbed down the rope she felt herself suddenly seized by some one from behind, and at once fainted with fright when she saw that he was not Nasir but a stranger. The robber was almost equally surprised to see a beautiful girl instead of the robber he had expected ; but at once he put her upon his shoulder and made off, bringing her to the place where his fellow robbers were. They gathered round her and, seeing her beauty, applauded and congratulated Sām greatly. The noise which they made brought the maiden to her senses, and she found herself in the midst of a group of villains, who caressed her, to her great disgust. Then, to celebrate the event, they made the girl be their cup-bearer and hand round wine to them. She herself drank very little, but constantly kept their glasses full while they sang and talked. As she walked from one to another with the wine, Sām became smitten with her charms and determined to keep the girl for himself. At last, when they all lay drunk with wine, Kihtar, the robber who had carried her off, in his drunkenness thought to himself, ' I had all the trouble of carrying her off. Why should she

belong to Sām and not to me ? ' Full of this
thought he rose slowly, tottered to his feet, drew
out a dagger, and stabbed every one of his fellow
scoundrels as they lay unconscious on the ground.
Then taking them one by one, he threw them into
a well that was in the middle of the courtyard
of the house, and into which the robbers used to
throw all their victims.

When he had finished his task he went to the
girl, who was in another room, listening in great
fear to what was happening, and said to her :
' I brought you, and am I to let any one else keep
you ? Look, I have killed them all ; now come
with me.' The girl saw his drunken state, and,
hoping to escape, went with him to another house
which he had in the neighbourhood ; and there
they remained.

Let us now return to Nasir, whom we left fast
asleep under the wall of the vizier's palace. When,
in an hour or so, he awoke and saw the rope
dangling against the wall, but without any sign of
Nasrat, he knew that their plan had miscarried.
In great trepidation he ran from street to street,
thinking that somehow she had failed to see him
and was now searching for him. But he found no
clue. As may be imagined, the companions of the
vizier's daughter were as alarmed as Nasir when
they awoke to find that she had disappeared. They
ran to her mother and told her what had occurred,
and she, tearing her hair and her clothes with
grief, told the vizier. In great distress the vizier
arose and sent out his servants in search of Nasrat,
but though they sought nearly the whole day they
found no trace of her.

At last, one of Nasrat's servant-maids, who had

seen her mistress's behaviour and knew that she
was in love with Nasir, came to the vizier and
related her suspicions to him.   At once the
vizier sent to Mansur bidding him to produce
Nasir.   The butcher himself in his alarm sought
everywhere for his friend but could not find him,
although he wandered about far into the night.   He
was compelled at last to go to the vizier and confess
that he had failed.   The minister, in rage at this,
immediately called his jailers and ordered them to
suspend the youth by his arms and leave him hung
up for three days, that he might be a warning to
others.   At the end of that time the jailers were
to cut down Mansur and bring him to the minister.

Meantime Nasir, who was by this time searching
the roads outside the town, had chanced upon
a company of people from the town.   In the course
of conversation he heard them talk of himself, who
had disappeared, and of Mansur, who had been
hung up by his arms for three days.   On hearing
this, Nasir resolved that he could not leave his
friend to suffer on his account, and turned back
to the city.   By the time he arrived it was quite
dark, but he made his way to the centre of the
town, and there saw Mansur hanging, with
a number of guards watching him.   They were all
awake, so that for the moment there was no hope of
rescue.   He therefore went into the shop of a neighbouring confectioner, and bought a tray full of
sweets.   Over these he poured a powerful soporific
drug and went up to the guard.   Immediately they
seized him, and asked where he was going so late,
and what he was doing.   He replied to their
satisfaction, but as he was going they took away
from him the tray of sweets which he had, and

began eating them. At this he set up a cry and asked them why they were eating his sweets. But they paid no heed and went on eating. When at last he got possession of his tray, he concealed himself round a corner and waited for the drug to take effect. It was not long before they were all asleep, and, as soon as he was sure of their helplessness, Nasir went up to Mansur, untied the rope by which he was suspended and released him. Then in his place the two friends hung up the chief of the guard, who was utterly overcome by the drug.

Once they had done this they made off together, Nasir on the way telling Mansur the whole story of the vizier's daughter, and what had happened to himself. Mansur then said, ' We had better go and conceal ourselves separately; for, if we are caught, terrible tortures await us.' He himself thereupon went and hid, but Nasir, not greatly caring what happened to him, continued to search for his sweetheart. By dawn he had gone some distance and sat down to rest by a well. As he sat there thinking of his woes a dervish approached, and saluting him asked for alms. ' I am weak and hungry, and have nothing wherewith to buy food. I have a family too. Can you not help me ? ' Now the dervish was in truth only the scoundrel Kihtar who had carried off the vizier's daughter, but Nasir did not know this, took pity on him, and gave him three dinars. He pretended to offer up prayer for Nasir, but while doing so poured a strong drug into the well and then drew some of the water in a cup, intending to drug Nasir and rob him at his leisure. Producing a loaf of bread and the water he turned to Nasir and said : ' Will you not, in return for your kindness, share my meal with me?' The young butcher could not refuse a piece of bread. When he had eaten and drunk a mouthful of the water, the dervish said, 'I have a room quite near, will you not come and rest there awhile?' But as Nasir rose to his feet the drug began to take effect, and he fell back senseless. Had it not been for the alms he had given, the scoundrel would have killed him where he lay, but instead he contented himself by searching the unconscious youth and taking from him the two purses of gold that he had received from the vizier's daughter.

Kihtar then returned home and displayed his booty to Nasrat, who recognized the purses as her own and asked: 'Whence did you obtain these?' He replied, 'I met a man on the road and gave him a drug. When he was unconscious I was about to kill him but I took pity on him, for he was a generous youth, and I took away this money that he had.' The girl, on hearing this, at once suspected that the youth could be no other than Nasir. After a little while the robber went off to gloat over his plunder and to hide it. Immediately, Nasrat took his drug and poured it into a goblet of wine, and when he returned gave it to him to drink. In a few moments the robber was fast asleep, and, as he lay there, Nasrat took his dagger and cut off his head, then ran as hard as she could to the well where he had told her that he had found Nasir.

When she reached the spot the girl found her lover still lying unconscious. She sat down by him and raised his head on to her lap, trying by every means in her power to arouse him. After a little while Nasir came to himself, and looking round beheld Nasrat. In their intense joy at beholding one another again, both of them burst into tears, but soon they calmed themselves, and related to each other what had occurred to them. The girl then led her lover back to the robber's room to show him where Kihtar lay dead ; at which sight Nasir greatly rejoiced.

In a very short time Nasrat had clothed herself in a man's garments and together they set off to a neighbouring village, where Nasir bought two horses and saddles, together with some provisions. They rode for several days until at last they reached Nasir's town. There the youth made for his own house and was filled with joy to see his friends again. Nasrat again resumed her ordinary attire and consented to marry Nasir ; and they lived together in great happiness for the rest of their lives.

Shirzad was delighted with this story and caressed his wife in his pleasure. Then they fell to eating and drinking, and again the slaying of Bihzad was postponed. On the sixth day the court moved to the pavilion of Mushtari, which is Jupiter, and resumed their feast. In the midst of their rejoicings Shirzad remembered the matter of Bihzad. At once he summoned his servants and said : ' Bring Bihzad, that I may exact satisfaction from him.' Gulshad heard this and threw herself at the king's feet. ' Your Majesty,' she said, remembering a story, ' we are to-day seated in the pavilion of Mushtari, which is one of the stars of Fortune.' Thereupon Shirzad placed a goblet of wine before her, but she said, ' How can I drink wine when you desire to slay my father ? This pavilion of Mushtari is dedicated to joy and

good fortune, as you will see from the story of the
Qazi who found himself under its influence.'
Shirzad asked, ' What was that ? ' and Gulshad
thereupon began

THE TALE OF THE QAZI

It is related that in Damascus there was a very
learned Qazi who was yet young and of handsome
appearance.   One day he was riding about the
town on horseback, when he came into the street
where the king's palace stood. Glancing up he saw
that upon the roof of a royal lodge a beautiful
girl was looking at him carefully. Now the girl,
Mastur, was a favourite concubine of the king's,
and was possessed of the greatest perfection of
beauty. She had no sooner looked at the Qazi
than she fell deeply in love with him, and at the
same moment the Qazi too was smitten with love
for Mastur. As he passed underneath the wall
where he sat, the lady leaned over and threw down
a golden orange which she had in her hand. The
Qazi caught it and stopped a moment to thank her
for her favour. But he was afraid to stay too long
for fear of being seen, and so departed ; but he
left his heart and soul behind him. He returned
home greatly excited and with his mind full of
visions. All night long he remained awake,
dreaming of his love and planning how to see her
again.

For her part Mastur too was filled with grief
when the Qazi departed, and schemed how she was
to see her beloved again. The next day she again
ascended to the roof and, as she hoped, she soon
espied the Qazi riding towards the palace wall,

where he expected to find Mastur. He stopped
only for a moment when he reached the spot; then
was compelled· to depart again. For ten days
they continued in this way to see each other, but
at last, one day, one of the king's slave-girls, who
was in his confidence, came on to the roof and saw
Mastur seated there. Approaching she rebuked
her and said, ' Why do you sit here where all men
pass, and where you are in the sight of all ? ' When
she advanced a little farther she saw the handsome
Qazi stationed there. At once turning full of
reproach to her mistress, she said, ' You are
playing at love with the Qazi of the town. Do you
think the king will not know of it ? ' She continued
thus to scold till her mistress was in tears. Then
Mastur, holding out a gem-encrusted perfume box
of great value, said to her, ' It is too late now,
you know of my love and you must help me.'
When the servant saw the casket she was placated
and said, ' Be reassured ; I will arrange a meeting
between you and the Qazi, when you may talk to
your heart's content.' Then she said, ' To-morrow
when the king goes riding, pretend to be ill and
moan aloud. But allow no one to remain in your
room ; pretend that you wish to remain quiet and
that voices will disturb you. By hook or by crook
I will bring the Qazi to you.'

The next day, accordingly, Mastur pretended
to be ill and moaned aloud, but allowed no one to
remain in her room, saying, ' People's voices
disturb me, and I cannot bear to hear them.' When
she was alone the slave-girl came to her and said :
' I am now going to bring the Qazi,' and then went
off to the Qazi's house. When she was admitted
she said to him : ' I have something to tell you in

private.' The Qazi took her into a private room and she there told him her errand. ' The king's favourite concubine', said she, ' has sent me for you. She is pretending to be ill, and I have come out under the pretence of bringing to her a wise woman skilled in medicine. You must now dress yourself as a woman and put on a heavy veil, so that we can go to her together.'

The Qazi joyfully agreed to the scheme. The slave-girl dressed him in a woman's clothes, arranged his hair, and finally, giving him a veil for his face, took him with her. When they reached the palace she was asked : ' Who is this woman ? ' To which she gave reply that it was a woman who had come to cup Mastur, and thus brought the pretended doctor into the apartment where the slave-girl lay. There she sat for a moment and then departed, saying that she would return at night. So all day the lovers remained talking of their love, happy in each other's company.

Towards nightfall news was brought that the king had arrived. There was no chance of letting the Qazi unperceived out of the palace, so the slave-girl, who had come to announce the king's arrival, took the Qazi quickly to a room near by in which the monarch kept his treasures. In it there stood a number of large coffers, some full and some empty. Into one of these latter the slave-girl put the Qazi and then locked it. A few moments later the king entered Mastur's apartment, and seeing her lying down asked what ailed her. She replied, ' I have been sick and have had a headache. But a woman has been here and has cupped one of my veins and I am better now.' The king sat down, asked for drink, and for a time remained there in converse.

Now it happened that a gang of robbers had determined to break into the palace that night and steal some of the king's treasures. Coming to the palace wall they threw up a rope and climbed on to the roof; then letting themselves down into the courtyard they entered the treasure room. The first coffer they reached chanced to be that which held the Qazi. They tried to raise it, and finding how heavy it was they at once assumed it was full of gold. With a great effort they managed to lift it on to the roof and then down to the street. There two men took hold of it, and, each in turn carrying it on his back, they made for their abode. On the way they saw that the night watchmen were coming towards them, so they concealed themselves hastily in a deep gateway, which happened to be that of the chief magistrate. There they sat till the watchmen had passed, and were just about to take up their burden and continue their way when the door behind them opened and a slave-girl appeared holding a lighted lamp. Hearing a noise outside the gate she had come to see if the gate was secure, but at sight of her the robbers fled guiltily, leaving the box behind them. The girl advanced in surprise to examine the great coffer. She tried it, but it was securely fastened; and so, going into the house, she told her mistress what had happened. They came out again together and with great difficulty carried the coffer into the house. Then with the first instrument that came to hand they prised off the lid. To their terrified amazement they saw in it their own town Qazi, dressed in woman's clothes. The chief magistrate was at the time in his own apartment with a number of friends who were feasting with him, and the noise of hammering was drowned by their revelry. But at any moment the magistrate might appear. His wife, who had a great regard for the Qazi, assisted him out of the coffer and hurried him quietly to her own room, where she asked him how he had come to be in his present plight. He answered: ' As I was sitting alone at home, two or three men, who are enemies of mine, broke in, collected all my valuables, and carried them off. They also dressed me in women's clothes, put me into this box, and took me with them. Fate decided that they should leave me here, while they themselves departed. Heaven be praised that it brought me into your gracious presence ! '

As they talked, they heard the footsteps of the magistrate returning to his wife's room. In great alarm she said to him : ' My husband had better not find you in your present garb. Here is an empty wine-jar. Conceal yourself in it till he is asleep and then I will let you out.'

When the magistrate came in, it was clear that he had drunk a great deal too much wine and that he was very quarrelsome. He turned crossly to his wife and in a loud voice abused her, saying that she cared nothing for him or the household, and was constantly talking with men with whom she had no business. ' I'll find a way of punishing you,' he concluded. His wife gave him in return as good as she got, and rated him soundly : ' You go away every night,' said she, ' and fill yourself with wine. Then when you come home you do nothing but abuse me. What is more, you scarcely ever carry out your duty of magistracy during the day. If the Qazi became aware of this, it would be I that could talk of punishment, not you.' As she said this the magistrate's anger was violently roused, and picking up a stone that was lying on the ground he threw it at his wife. His drunken aim was so bad, however, that instead of hitting his wife the stone crashed against the wine-jar and broke it into pieces. Immediately the woman threw herself upon her husband and struggled with him, while the slave-girl, seizing her opportunity, took the Qazi by the hand, ran with him to her room, where she hastily covered him with a large woman's cloak and took him to the door. As they emerged into the morning light, the magistrate came running after them and furiously asked the slave-girl to tell him where she was going and who the other woman was. She replied, ' She is a neighbour of ours and is going to the Qazi's house with a complaint. I am accompanying her because it is still very early.' After some further conversation the magistrate turned back into his house while the Qazi made his way home, and there, having put on his ordinary garments, seated himself again upon the seat of justice in pursuit of his daily business.

Shirzad laughed at the story and ordered wine to be brought, and they sat and feasted. For that day also the slaying of Bihzad was postponed. On the seventh day they moved to the pavilion of Zuhal, which is Saturn, and resumed their feast. When Shirzad had had his fill of wine he remembered Bihzad and told his servants to bring the wretch and hang him at once. Gulshad heard the order and, seating herself at her husband's feet, drank a glass of wine with him and said, ' It is ill policy to hasten, for patience is the best of all virtues. Moreover we are now sitting in the pavilion dedicated to Zuhal, whose influence is dangerous. But it is not always so, for the destinies which it decrees are many. For example, in the strange story of the enchanted isle, which if you will permit me I will relate.' 'Relate it,' said Shirzad, and Gulshad at once began the story of

THE ENCHANTED ISLAND

In the island of Samarat there was once a wise king named Jamirun. In his service he had two excellent viziers, Afkarun and Sikalun, and a hundred islands were under his sway. One day the desire seized him to go a-hunting on one of the islands of his realm. He invited to go with him twenty of his intimates from amongst his nobles, and also his two viziers. Two ships were fitted out. In the first the king embarked with his viziers, leaving the courtiers and servants to follow in the second; and both ships set sail.

They had not been long upon the open sea when a furious storm arose, with most violent wind accompanied by heavy rain. They could do nothing against it, and were forced to run before it for several days. When the storm at last abated the king's ship had lost sight of the other. They had not reckoned on being away from land for so long, and the king decided to land on the first island that was sighted in order to obtain more food and water. After a day's sailing they saw an island on the horizon, which, as they approached it, appeared to them to be very pleasant. The whole island was a mass of green and well covered with trees, and from the ship many rivers and springs were visible, glistening in the sunshine.

The landing did not belie their first view. The trees and verdure were delightful, and the air was filled with the songs of innumerable bulbuls. The first thought of the king was for a drink of fresh water, and he made his way with his two viziers towards a beautiful pool round which great trees grew. At the foot of one of these he sat down, and was about to dip his hand into the water, when a terrible voice came from the tree and said : ' Do not drink of this water, if you value your life.' The king bounded up with amazement. How could a voice come out of the heart of the tree ? Turning towards it he saw that the tree was shaking violently, and a moment later a peri emerged. Her skin, he saw, was black, but her head was covered with glistening white hair.

Terror seized Jamirun at the sight. Soon recovering himself, however, he went up and greeted the peri, who returned his salute by a nod of the head. Somewhat reassured by this, the king and his viziers seated themselves again, and after some moments, addressing the peri, said : ' Pray tell us, what is this fountain ? What strange property has it, and why did you warn me not to drink of it ? ' ' This water ', replied she, ' is such that if you plunged your hand into it you could never withdraw it, and if you drank of it you would be turned to stone. If you do not believe me,' she added, ' take a branch of the tree and dip it into the water.' They approached the tree and broke off a branch, starting back in fear when they heard the tree groan as if in pain. The king dipped the branch into the water, but he could not withdraw

it, although he put out all his strength, and, in
spite of him, the branch remained floating there.

Tired at last with his efforts, the king sat down,
and calling his vizier Afkarun said to him : ' Ask
her to show you some miracle too.' Afkarun
thereupon approached the peri and asked to be
shown some marvel. At his words, she put her
hand upon his head, and he, falling upon his face,
found himself transported to another island,
infinitely more beautiful even than the first. On
all sides were streamlets and fountains which spread
a delightful freshness in the air ; the earth was
carpeted with the greenest and softest of verdure,
and from the many trees hung the most beautiful
and delicious-looking fruits.

The vizier, full of strange joy, began running
about, eating the fruit and seeing on all sides
new and strange sights. Soon he came upon
a troop of genii who, in the twinkling of an eye,
had run up to him and held him, while each in
turn rubbed his face against that of the disgusted
Afkarun. Then they led him to a palace, where,
seated on a throne, he saw their chief, a female
genie. When they entered, she motioned them to
bring Afkarun to her, bade him be seated beside
her, and then, as he sat down, she took a handful
of dust and poured it over his head. At sight of
this the genii burst out into transports of joy, and
leapt and danced and laughed with merriment.
' We congratulate you,' said they, to the astonished
vizier ; ' you may be certain that now your
happiness is assured, for our sovereign has poured
dust upon your head. She has no husband, and
by her action she has given proof of a desire to
accept you as her betrothed. Hasten, therefore,

and ask her to be your wife, and so live happily
for ever, for all that you wish will be granted to
you. But if, on the other hand, you refuse this
happy adventure, she will cut you into small
pieces.'

The vizier was compelled, by his desire to avoid
the fate that would befall him upon his refusal,
to put a good face upon the matter, and asked
the queen of the genii to be his wife. So, with
much drinking of wine and feasting and rejoicing
they celebrated the wedding.

In due course a son was born to them whose
body was human, but who had the head of a div;
yet the mother loved the child greatly. One day,
when the boy was about five years old, Afkarun
remembered his king Jamirun, and heaved a deep
sigh. The child, hearing it, came to play with his
father and comfort him, but Afkarun was sad and
roughly pushed the boy away. The queen of the
genii, who was standing by, was greatly angered
at this, and ordered her slaves to fling Afkarun
into the water. The unfortunate vizier was cast
into the lake, and sank out of their sight; but he,
to his great astonishment, found in a moment that
his head was pushing through the earth, and as he
opened his eyes and looked about him, he saw that
he was in the exact spot where the fairy had put
her hand on his head, and where he had left the
king. His amazement was increased when he saw
that they were still there. He saluted them, and
when he had seated himself by their side the king
asked where he had been and what he had seen.
Afkarun thereupon told his story and was somewhat annoyed when the king told him that he had
only been a moment gone.

Jamirun's appetite was whetted by what he had heard. Turning to the peri he asked for another miracle. She turned to the other vizier, made a movement with her hand over his head, and immediately he disappeared into the earth from the sight of his two companions. In his place they saw emerging a great tree which grew larger every moment, pushing out branches on all sides and being gradually covered with leaves. A few moments later the tree burst into bloom, and the sweet scent of the blossom filled the garden with fragrance. Gradually the blossoms dropped and fruits appeared which grew and ripened before the king's eyes. When they were mature, each of the fruits exactly resembled a man's head in shape, the mouth, ears, and forehead being all completely formed. After all had appeared, one of the fruits opened its mouth and greeted the king respectfully. At a sign from the fairy's hand the fruit fell at the king's feet. He picked it up and ate a piece of it, but not finding it to his taste, threw the rest away. Immediately the fairy stretched out her hand towards the tree ; from her pointing finger a flame leapt out, which set the tree in a blaze. The fire spread in a moment to all parts of it, each branch sending out flames of a different colour from the rest, and emitting the most delightful scents. The flames at last enveloped the whole tree, which, in a few moments, lay in ashes on the ground. The ashes gathered themselves together into a heap, and out of the midst of them appeared the vanished vizier.

The minister had no sooner emerged than the king eagerly asked him what he had seen. ' As soon as I disappeared from before your Majesty,' said Sikalun, ' I found myself in a garden that was a very paradise on earth. Sitting in it upon a glorious throne, I saw a king, whom I saluted, and to whom I spoke, but I received no answer from him. As I spoke, I felt myself being lifted to a great height into the air and could see the earth like a gleaming point below me. I saw angels' robes all about me as I moved, and soon I was being clothed with heavenly garments, constantly renewed. A great cleanness filled the whole universe. When I cried out at the brilliant light it was immediately followed by deep darkness. At the same time I felt myself being stripped of the celestial robes, and was filled with grief at it. I groaned, and for a moment lost my senses through the intensity of my pain; and when I came to myself again and opened my eyes, I saw you sitting there.'

Again the king turned to the fairy and said : ' Pray let me now in my turn behold marvels.' ' So be it,' was the reply, ' I will show you that of which your mind could not of itself conceive. Rise, go towards that forest and enter it.' Jamirun did so, and had only taken a few steps when he saw before him a dome of white marble. Entering it he saw a maiden of bewitching beauty seated upon a couch. She rose at his entrance, greeted the king and took his hand ; then bidding the king sit at her side upon the couch she began to converse with him. While she spoke, the king felt that the couch was in motion upwards towards the top of the dome. He thought in his alarm that they would be crushed against it, but the roof opened and let them pass. Higher and higher they soared, then suddenly found themselves upon solid earth in the midst of a delightful garden. The king turned for an instant to admire a mass of blossom, and when he looked round again both couch and maiden had vanished. Thinking that they had somehow been moved amongst the flowering shrubs, he began to look about him on all sides, but in the beauty of what he saw he soon forgot everything else.

Flowers of all kinds came upon his delighted vision. The leaves of the trees seemed to dance with joy, and the roses smiled at him. But as he stretched out his hand to pluck a flower, the thorns suddenly elongated themselves like arrows and shot out against him. The king withdrew in alarm and fled from the garden. After some travel along a desert road he came upon another garden, which seemed filled with joyousness. The whole garden was covered with narcissus, which budded and burst into full blossom as the king approached. But as he bent down to admire a bloom it burst into tears, and the next, and the next, until every flower in the garden wept miserably. Again the king fled, and came to another garden, in which the flowers were all tulips of the most fragrant scent. Soon he was overcome by the heavy fragrance and fled again. A fourth garden appeared in his way. Entering it he saw that lilies were planted everywhere. In the midst of them were ten maidens who sang and recited enchanting verse. At his coming they approached and greeted him : ' Sire,' said they, ' if you wish for the highest happiness stay with us here for ten years, and you will wish for naught that cannot be fulfilled.' But the king would not tarry even in that place of delights. He hurried on and came at last to a great tree, whose enormous branches spread out in all directions and whose multitude of leaves cast a deep shadow upon the ground. Under it was a spring of pure sweet water, the very Fountain of Light.

At the side of the spring a couch was placed, and on it reposed a maiden whose appearance soothed his weary eyes and whose look drew him to sit beside her. She asked him whence he had come and how it was that he journeyed there. The king began to speak to her of love. But she turned to him and said : ' None can woo me who has not bathed and been purified in the Fountain of Light. Dive into it : you will emerge without a stain, and then you may speak to me of love.'

Instantly he arose and plunged into the fountain. But instead of floating again he found himself drawn under water, where he lost all consciousness. When he awoke he was under the dome of white marble. Out of this he came running, and was soon once more in the company of his two viziers. As he sat down, the peri disappeared into the magic tree, which closed up and became again as it was on their arrival at the island.

Then the company set out to find food and water. Without further adventure they gathered great quantities of fruit, filled their vessels with sweet water, and on returning to the sea they found their ship as they had left it. They embarked and set sail for their own country, which they soon reached without harm. The king again ascended his throne, and lived as he had always done in the past, in all luxury and happiness.

When Gulshad had told this story the king was delighted and ordered another feast. The next day (the eighth) Shirzad moved his court to the

pavilion of the fixed stars, where they resumed
their feasting. In the midst of it, Shirzad remembered the matter of his mother and the vizier
Bihzad. Summoning his servants he said, ' Bring
me Bihzad. To-day without fail I will punish him.'
Gulshad approached as he said this, and seating
herself before him she cried out : ' O King, to-day
we are seated in the pavilion of the fixed stars, and
wondrous stories are told of their influences and of
the happenings under them. I have in mind an
amazing story which will prove what I say. If you
agree I will tell it you.' ' Very well,' said Shirzad,
' relate it.' So the girl began the story of

SAYYARA, THE SON OF THE KING OF THE GREEKS

In the kingdom of Greece there was once a king
that had a son, Sayyara. Although he was a youth
of great beauty and talents, from time to time evil
genii possessed him, so that he wandered about
for two or three days as though demented. Now
the king had two trusty slaves whom he had
appointed to watch over his son day and night, so
that at the periods when he was possessed by
genii no harm should come to him. One night,
the prince, accompanied by his attendants, went up
on to the flat roof of the palace and sat down in
a corner. After a long period of watching the two
attendants fell asleep, while Sayyara remained
awake. As he gazed about him he saw towards
the east a gay company of beautiful damsels, all
dressed in the richest brocade and each carrying in
her hand a lighted torch. Leaping and dancing

they advanced towards him, but without making a sound. Suddenly there appeared a litter, whose curtains were drawn aside. In it he saw a maiden, whose beautiful face shone more brightly than the sun, and who, in charm and delightfulness, was beyond compare. As they approached she put out her head and watched her companions dancing and playing till the morning, when they all vanished.

The prince was greatly excited at what he had seen, and when the servants awoke from their sleep they brought him down from the roof and took him to his father. The king was sad to see how greatly his son's malady was increased. He attempted to speak with him, but the prince made no reply, and when night came he again went on to the roof and sat down in the same place. When the slaves were asleep, Sayyara turned his watchful regard towards the East again, and once more he saw the company of beauteous maidens, richly dressed, with lanterns in their hands, and speaking no word. In a little while the litter also appeared, bearing that damsel of surpassing beauty who had sat in it the previous night. The prince remained as before, watching their dancing and playing till dawn, when they again vanished from his sight.

Sayyara's exclamations roused the servants, who took him down from the roof to their master, who saw that his son's malady was still further increased, and who was immeasurably saddened to receive no reply when he spoke to him. For seven nights the prince remained upon the roof seeing his visions, while his madness increased day by day. The sorrow of the king and his companions was extreme, and they cast about everywhere for a remedy, but without success.

At last, a wise vizier of the king said that he knew a clever and skilful physician, one Muayyad, who was of the highest trustworthiness. The king thereupon told the vizier to go to the physician and bring him to the palace. This the vizier did, on the way telling Muayyad of the prince's madness. When they arrived they went directly to the king, who treated the physician most kindly, and offered him a great sum of money and many gifts to cure his son.

The physician, however, would accept nothing, but asked to see the prince. On examining him carefully he found that the youth was afflicted by genii and that his brain had dried up. Turning to the king he told him of his diagnosis and said : ' Out to sea there is a charming and delightful island of pleasant climate. In it there is a spring, whose waters will restore to health any sufferer from madness that drinks of them there, but the waters lose their beneficent qualities if they are removed far from their source. The prince must be taken to live in that excellent climate for some days, eating suitable foods and drinking of those waters. It may be that Allah will then drive away this disease.' The king at once decided to send his son, and asked the physician if he would consent to accompany the prince to the island. On his agreeing to do so, the king, as soon as possible, fitted out an expedition and dispatched Muayyad with the prince and a company of attendants.

A long voyage without incident brought the party at last to their destination, where the physician, soon after landing, commenced his treatment. For three days all went well, and then the physician, while taking a walk, found that

a party of strangers had landed and had pitched
a fine tent. On going up to discover who these
people were, Muayyad saw lying upon a couch
a most beautiful maiden bound hand and foot.
In great astonishment he asked the attendants
who the maiden was, and why she was bound.
They told him that she was the daughter of the
king of the peris, and that she had been struck
with madness so violent that fetters had to be
put upon her. 'We have tried all methods of
treatment without success,' they continued, 'and
are taking her now to the Greek physician Muayyad,
the fame of whose skill has reached us. We had
been several days upon our voyage when we came
to this island, and were so attracted by the sight
of it that we have landed here to rest. In two days
we will go on to consult the physician.'

Muayyad smiled at this, and thereby angered the
peris, who thought he was mocking their princess.
But he calmed them by saying that he smiled
because of the strange chance that brought him,
Muayyad, whom they were anxious to consult, to
that very island. They were greatly rejoiced at
his words, and took him to see the maiden. He
found that she was beautiful beyond imagining,
and undertook to apply his treatment to her. He
then told the peris that he had come to the island
with the prince of Greece, who was possessed
by genii, and was also being treated there. 'I
will arrange', said he, 'to bring them together,
and treat them with appropriate food and drink
for forty days, and will try thus to drive out their
malady.' To this they replied that he was at
liberty to do as he desired. He thereupon
departed, and in a short time came back bringing

Sayyara with him, in order to present him to the
princess. Seating the prince before the maiden,
the physician busied himself with his remedies and
medicines. Meantime, in spite of their madness,
the two sick people had fallen deeply in love with
one another, and during the forty days of their
treatment their love increased. On the last day
the physician announced that they were now ready
to drink of the spring-water, and hoped that by
Allah's aid the genii of madness would be driven
out of them and that his patients would return to
sanity. He took them to the brink of the pool,
and commanded them to plunge in and drink
the waters. This they did, and were at once
healed. Their love, however, remained, and they
could not bring themselves to part. At last, after
waiting three days for the last traces of the disease
to disappear, the physician wished to set out for
home, but both his patients steadfastly refused
to move from the island. The peris pleaded with
their princess and said : ' Now that you are cured
it is fitting that you return home, for your father
and mother will be greatly disturbed at your
absence and will be awaiting you.' She replied :
' I cannot bring myself to separate from Sayyara.
Go yourselves, and leave me here.' Their protests
were of no avail, and at last two or three of
them went back to the land of the peris to inform
their king of his daughter's decision, while the rest
remained. So, too, the Greek prince insisted on
remaining upon the island, and the physician sent
some of his attendants to inform the king of the
Greeks of Sayyara's decision.

The king and queen of the peris and the king of
the Greeks were all greatly vexed at the news

brought to them, and decided to set out to the
island to see that their instructions were obeyed.
The two parties landed on the island together, and
the king of the peris took his daughter aside and
lavished caresses on her, while urging her to dis-
continue her love for the prince. But his commands
were of no avail, and he thought sorrowfully that
his daughter had disgraced him. But when the king
of the Greeks approached, he embraced him and
they entered into conversation. Finally Sayyara
was summoned, and when he arrived he at once
won the affection of the king of the peris. The two
monarchs remained on the island for two or three
days; then the king of the Greeks, summoning
Muayyad, the physician, said to him: 'It is
disastrous that my son and this maiden are in love
with each other and cannot be separated. Go
with all the wisdom at your command, and place
the matter before the king of the peris.' Muayyad
did as he was commanded, and pleaded for the
prince. The king of the peris, however, refused
to hear him and said: 'What relationship can
there be between a peri and a mortal?' But the
physician pleaded so wisely with him that at last he
consented to the marriage. Thereupon a great
feast was prepared and the betrothal of the prince
and the princess was celebrated. A few days later
the king of the peris departed, while his daughter
accompanied her husband and the king of the
Greeks to their home.

When Gulshad had finished her story, the king
showed his delight by ordering more wine, and
they passed the rest of their time feasting, so that
the punishment of Bihzad was again forgotten.

On the ninth day they moved to the pavilion dedicated to the highest heaven, and there sat feasting. Suddenly Shirzad recalled the matter of Bihzad, and told the servants to bring the culprit that he might exact vengeance. Again Gulshad heard what was afoot, but she knew that the conjunction of stars which concerned her father would that day be dissolved, and he would be freed from evil influence. As she sat at Shirzad's side he said to her: ' You know the wrong your father did to my mother: it is impossible to release him. For several days now I have delayed his punishment for your sake, but to-day I must exact retribution.' Gulshad loosened her tongue and said : ' May thy life and glory be everlasting ! This is the ninth pavilion in which you have taken up your lodging, and in which you busy yourself with pleasure, may it long continue ! It is no place for bloodshed. I have a story concerning the highest heaven, which I will relate if you permit.' Shirzad commanded her to say on, and she began the story of

THE PRINCE OF KASHMIR AND THE HOLY SHEIKH

It is told that in the depths of the kingdom of Kashmir there dwelt a sheikh endowed with all the excellences of character and knowledge. He was the most learned man of his day, and no science remained hidden from him. His abode was in a cave hidden amongst the mountains, where he spent his life in prayer and worship.

Now the king of Kashmir had a handsome son who was devoted to the chase. One day the prince was hunting with a number of attendants, and, finding game in abundance, the company separated. The prince with four knights rode after a gazelle, which made off into the mountains. They had galloped some distance when suddenly a great dragon appeared, from whose jaws issued fiery breath. As the knights came in view the monster sent out a flame and burned them up in a twinkling. He was turning upon the prince, when, from the heart of the mountain, a mighty roar was heard and the dragon was turned to stone. At the terrible sound the prince was filled with trembling fear and fell to the ground. Suddenly a hand appeared, picked him up, and carried him before the sheikh. In a few moments he came to himself, and when he opened his eyes he saw before him the venerable old man, and stood up to greet him. The sheikh replied courteously : ' Be of good cheer, my son, for Allah's regard is upon you, and He turned to stone the dragon that was about to attack you. Now that you are safe here, show your gratitude to Allah by putting off your princely form for a time and by devoting yourself to poverty and worship. Thus you may discover the secrets of the hidden, reach the world of the spirit, and thereby bring within your grasp faith and the future world.'

The prince agreed to remain with the sheikh, and the latter then told him that in his cave was a spring. ' Go to it,' he continued, ' bathe in it for two or three days according to the holy will, and dedicate yourself continually, so that you may enter the path of poverty and thereafter give proof of your holy state.'

The prince arose, went to the cave, and there

bathed obediently and reverently. For three days he continued his ablutions, praying and devoting himself to religious practice all the time.

Meanwhile, the attendants who had not been consumed by the dragon were seeking everywhere for the prince. They saw the burnt bodies of their comrades, but of him there was no sign. Thinking that he too had been destroyed, they returned to their master and informed him of his son's horrible fate. In great sorrow the king himself came to the mountain to seek the prince, but could see no trace of him. Full of woe he returned home, and for forty days mourned for his son.

During this time the prince remained with the sheikh in prayer and devotion; and gradually learned the essential secrets. One day while he was thus engaged, the old man told him to look about him, and as he did so he saw himself as a dove with wings and feathers, while the sheikh appeared to him as a white hawk. Suddenly the hawk began to soar above the earth, and the dove followed in flight towards the upper universe. At last they arrived in a garden covered with the most luxuriant verdure, beautiful as Paradise. In it walked a hundred thousand angels, going hither and thither on the green sward. The white hawk the whole time paid the greatest attention to his companion the dove; continuing their flight, they reached another place of delight, a rose-garden of wondrous beauty, in which were thousands of heavenly beings, who wandered to and fro while praising God. Amongst them the hawk went and walked, ever regarding them, with the dove following as his servitor.

As he moved about, the dove felt himself increasingly filled with happy thoughts and with divine love, and his soul was filled with delight, for he stood amongst a thousand angels pouring forth praises. Soon, with his tutor, the white hawk, he flew higher again and reached the upper world, a paradise full of red blossoms, whose scent and beauty were everywhere. Even as the voyagers looked, angels alighted on the flowers and devoted themselves to praises and contemplation of the divine mysteries.

Again the hawk and his companion flew away to another garden, this time of sandalwood and other scented trees, whence the dove beheld further visions of unearthly light. Now at last the dove's heart filled with purity and love, and, as he turned, he saw the hawk once more as a venerable sheikh seated in his house, while he himself had again assumed his human form. From thence onward he became the devoted slave of his pious tutor, and remained with him long, learning much.

Meantime the king remained full of woe at the loss of his son, and went his daily way full of longing. One night as he lay asleep he saw in a dream a genie, who spoke to him and said : ' Go towards the mountain of the dragon, and you will behold the monster, which will turn into stone at your approach. Advance from thence until you reach the cave of the sheikh, and there wait until the divine purpose be revealed to you.'

The next morning the king set forth, and to his joy he saw as he approached that the dragon was turned to stone. He advanced, then, to the cave of the sheikh, who by this time had died, and whose tomb lay in the midst of the cave. As the king entered he saw a young man deep in prayer, and waited until he should finish. The youth turned at the sound of footsteps, and to his intense joy he recognized his father, to whom he related his story, and told how he had become the attendant at the shrine. After three days of prayer they returned together to the capital.

When Gulshad had finished her story, the king expressed his great delight, and for that day, too, the slaying of Bihzad was put off. On the following day Gulshad summoned the merchant Asad and said to him : ' The evil conjunction has disappeared from the horoscope of Bihzad. I desire you to go to the king and ask pardon and forgiveness for him.' Asad and his companions thereupon went to the king, and after many entreaties persuaded him to pardon Bihzad and to draw the pen of forgiveness through his guilt, and for forty days thereafter they celebrated the joyful event in feasting and joy.

For forty years Shirzad reigned in all prosperity. Then one day the desire possessed him to hunt again in the forest. Taking a company of nobles with him he rode out. No sooner had they entered the trees than a lion sprang upon Shirzad, tore him from his horse and bore him away. The king did not fear, for he knew the ways of lions, and in a little while he seated himself upon the lion's back, took it by the ears and led it among the trees. His attendants lost sight of him, and though they sought everywhere no trace of him was ever found again. Gulshad, in great sorrow, mourned for him continually, and at last in deepest despair went up to the topmost tower of her castle with the intention of throwing herself to the ground. But, as she leapt, the wind caught her and carried her away, and no man knows whither she went.

[MS. Caps. Or. A. 4.]

KHURSHIDSHAH AND THE
PRINCESS OF CHINA

HALAB, a province in Syria, was once ruled by a king Marzubanshah and his vizier Haman. The king had rich treasures—silks from China, gold and rubies from Hindustan, and great herds of camels and horses; but yet he was unhappy, for he had no son to succeed him; and day and night he longed and prayed for one. One day Haman came upon him sitting downcast and sad upon his throne, and said: 'O King, why art thou unhappy? Everything is in thy power, and thy horoscope is strongly favourable. Thou hast a great empire and riches in abundance, and not an enemy in the world. Why then art thou downcast?' The king replied: 'All that thou sayest is true, but nought is well without a son. If I have no son, who is it that will maintain my throne in majesty when my fate overtakes me? A stranger will take my place, and my name will be buried.' The vizier replied: 'It is indeed as your Majesty says. He that hath no son hath no name, and his name disappears. No one asks, "Who are the administrators of the king?" but, "Who is his son?" "Who will sit on his throne in his place, and who lives in his stead?" But that is all in God's hand, and there is no help save in prayer and weeping.' The king replied: 'This indeed is truth that you speak, but I wish you to look well into my horoscope. Calculate the heavens and the influence of the stars, and see whether fate has a

son in store for me.' The vizier replied: ' I obey
your command.' So, rising and taking leave of the
king, he went to do his bidding, and soon after
returned, saying : ' I bound on to the loins of my
soul the girdle of your service, and employed all my
skill. In your horoscope I have seen that there
is a son for you, but the oyster that contains this
pearl is not of this land. In Iraq ', he continued,
' there is a king, Samaruk, who has a daughter,
Gulnar by name, more beautiful than the moon.
To him send a messenger to ask for his daughter in
marriage. She has already been married and has
borne a son, Farrukhruz, but his father has died.'
Marzubanshah rejoiced at the words of his vizier,
and straightway going to his treasury he prepared
a gift of sacks full of gold, ropes of pearls, a jewel-
studded crown in value beyond compute, a hundred
robes of all colours, and fifty slaves.   Then,
summoning his trusty courtier Jambur, he bade
him take the gift to Iraq, and ask as best he knew
for the hand of King Samaruk's daughter. ' And ',
said the king, ' go speedily.' Also the king gave
him a letter sealed with his seal, and he departed.

When he approached the capital of Iraq, news
was brought to King Samaruk that an ambassador
had come from Halab bearing a message. The
king was astonished. ' For ', said he to himself,
' what can this mean ? They have never before
sent me any ambassador or any message.' In this
state of wonderment he remained, while his troops
welcomed the stranger with due ceremonial and
accompanied him into the city. Immediately food
and fodder were provided, and, when Jambur had
rested somewhat from his journey, the king held
a court and sent a messenger to summon him.

When the ambassador approached the king's throne, he made obeisance and blessed him, and Samaruk made a sign that he was to be seated upon a golden throne. Young noblemen then brought in wine which was offered to all, on trays of gold and silver. When they had feasted, Jambur had the gifts brought in, and presented the letter which he had brought. This was opened and read by the king's vizier, who reported to Samaruk what it contained. The king was greatly pleased, and said that of all men in the world he could desire none better than Marzubanshah to be his son-in-law.

In course of time he prepared a caravan laden with rich merchandise; with it he sent a hundred slave-girls, and a hundred white slaves, and a hundred black slaves, and jewels without number. His daughter he set upon a beautiful Arab horse adorned with golden bells, and sent her, with her son Farrukhruz and attended by his vizier Shirwan, to the court of Marzubanshah. After a toilsome journey along the Euphrates river and across the great desert they reached Halab.

Marzubanshah celebrated his wedding with great splendour, and the princess Gulnar lived happily in Halab and bore the king a son, Khurshid-shah. The two young princes grew up together, spending their time in hunting and playing and feasting, and in listening to the music of the lute and the harp and in singing, and in all kinds of games; but of all sports they loved hunting the best.

Now when Khurshidshah reached the age of seventeen, he wished to celebrate his birthday by arranging a great hunting-party, which was to last

for a week. The king his father gladly permitted
this, and sent with him two companions of high
rank, and five thousand horsemen, with falcons and
hawks and hunting panthers, and they pitched
a gorgeous pavilion on the plains. Every day
they hunted, and every evening were brought in
gazelles and bustard and wild fowl of all kinds, on
which they feasted. Each morning they moved
farther from home.

It happened that early on the seventh morning
the prince desired to ride with his following. On
his way he came to a pleasant meadow, which
delighted him so much that he resolved not to hunt
that day, but to rest there and spend the time in
feasting. While they were pitching the tents the
prince said : ' I will go away with Farrukhruz until
you have got ready the camp.' So they departed,
but had not gone many steps when they saw a
beautiful wild ass, white as silver, with black lines
stretching from the tip of each ear down to its tail.
The prince, shouting to his brother to wait, immediately pursued it on his horse, trying with both
noose and arrow to bring down his quarry ; but
the wild ass was as swift as the wind, and no horse
could come near it nor arrow reach it. At length
it vanished. By this time Khurshidshah was far
from his friends and night had fallen. For a long
time he wandered in the darkness, uncertain where
his road lay, until at last from weariness he dropped
from his horse and slept where he was.

As he was preparing to ride home next morning,
the wild ass appeared again, and again the prince
set off in pursuit, and once more it vanished before
he could catch it. He wandered for many miles
until at last he came to a stretch of desert, a place

of barren hillocks of sand stretching as far as the eye could reach, with many stones and low thorny bushes. As he made his way slowly across the waste, to his amazement there came into view a beautiful tent, and as he came closer he saw that it was made of crimson satin, with silken ropes and tent-pegs of gold. A ring of jewels was set around it, and at the top of the tent-pole was perched a golden fish encrusted with precious stones. The flap of the tent was down, and no one was in sight. At last he reached the tent and cried out 'Salām', but no answer came, so he lifted up the flap and stepped in.

A glorious vision met his gaze. Lying asleep upon brocaded cushions he beheld a princess, whose closed eyes were like narcissi, cheeks like a rose, chin like a round ball in a well, and her neck short, while a hundred small folds fell under her chin. Her bosom was like a throne of silver, her arm short, and on every finger flashed jewelled rings.

Breathlessly the prince gazed upon her beauty, and in a moment his heart had left his body in his love. The world suddenly became bright to his eyes. To his heart he said : ' O heart, that once laughed at lovers, what hath possessed thee ? ' As he gazed, the princess opened her eyes, and seeing the handsome youth before her, she cried out : ' Who are you, and whence have you come here ? ' The prince was enchanted with her voice, and exclaimed : ' Be not afraid, I came to rest at your door. Who are. you ? Are you a houri that the gate-keeper of Paradise has sent to look at the earth, or are you the queen of the fairies ? In my life I have seen no one like you.' But she replied :

'O handsome youth, what is your concern with my origin?'

The prince was left speechless with surprise by this reply, and thought to himself; 'If only my horsemen were here I could carry her off with me, for if she will not go, I cannot, without shaming her, carry her off alone. Who can have brought her here? She must surely have some guard, but even if a thousand horsemen appear I must oppose them all, and will overcome them.' As he stood thinking thus, and glancing about him, he espied a golden pitcher full of water. At once he remembered his thirst, for he had not drunk water for a day and a night. Turning to the princess he craved her permission to take a drink, saying he was very thirsty. 'Why did you not drink?' said the maiden. 'Water is made to drink.' The prince stepped forward and took up the vessel. Scarcely had he placed it to his lips and taken one draught than his senses left him and he fell swooning to the floor.

Meantime Farrukhruz had returned to the camp and told the prince's followers that Khurshidshah had gone in pursuit of a wild ass and had not returned to the place appointed. He had now waited a whole day and night, and thought it would be advisable to go in search of the prince. Immediately the royal attendants flew to horse, and rode hard till they reached the top of a hill. There in front of them they beheld a valley, rough and desolate, which appeared to them as a portion of Hell. Soon they saw the prince lying amidst the stones and sand, and thought he must surely have fallen from his horse while chasing the wild ass, and been killed. But when they approached, they saw, to their joy, that the prince was alive. They waited, shading him till he was awake, and were amazed, when he opened his eyes, to hear him exclaim : ' Where is the princess and where the beautiful red tent, and what is this vile place of sand and stones ? ' When he at last realized what had happened he was inconsolable ; his courtiers tried to persuade him that it was all a dream or else that he had been deluded. ' For ', said they, ' no one can believe that any living creature could have dwelt in this desolate waste.'

Slowly they made their way back towards the palace, and the prince was bowed down with grief and despair, when suddenly he espied on his finger a ring, inscribed with mystic symbols and of curious design. Overjoyed, he cried aloud to his companions : ' Behold, does this not prove my story ? This must surely be a token of her love.'

They made the rest of the journey in great haste, and, having arrived home, they reported the whole matter to the king.

As time went on, the prince in his longing for the maiden fell desperately sick. The physicians did all in their power. The astrologers who were consulted assured the king that his son would be healed, would become a great king, and after many trials and sorrows would reach great fortune. But it was all of no avail. The prince became more sick than ever. The wise men of the palace suspected that the remedy lay in the ring, but none of them could read its secret. At last the king consulted his vizier, and asked : ' What can we do to heal my son ? ' The vizier replied : ' The only means lies in solving the mystery of the legend on the ring. Let the ring be hung in the market-place, and offer a thousand dinars of gold and a robe of honour to any one who can read it.' The king consented to this, and the ring was exposed to the crowds that thronged the bazaar; but none was found who could offer any clue.

After many days an old dervish with a ragged cloak upon his back and a staff in his hand came to the town, and seeing a great crowd gathered in the market-place he turned to a bystander and asked: 'Why is all this tumult, and why is this gold ring hung on high, and why do the criers proclaim that any one who can read the ring will be given a thousand dinars and a robe of honour? Give me the ring, and let me examine it.'

The crowd, on hearing this from the old man, laughed and jeered at him, saying: 'It is now four months that all the wise men of the earth, and all the nobles and priests, and men of high station and of low, have tried to read the mystery but have not succeeded. How can you hope to do it?' But the officers of the king heard what was happening, and making their way through the crowd brought the old man to where the king was seated. The monarch greeted him, and asked if he could read the inscription. 'Assuredly,' said he, 'and I know where the ring itself belongs.'

The king, accompanied by the dervish, then made his way to the palace, to the chamber where the prince lay. Seated there, the old man told his story thus: 'This ring belongs to the daughter of the Emperor of China. The maiden, whose name is Mah Pari, is beautiful as the full moon; but she has a nurse who is a powerful sorceress, and who, if she is not shown sufficient honour by the Emperor, carries off the princess to remote parts of the earth, to such places as that in which you saw her. Only when the king humbles himself to the sorceress does she bring the princess back. The ring is a talisman with magic power, which makes him who can read the signs thereon safe from her power. I have no doubt that the nurse makes matters so to fall out that kings and princes see the maiden and are at once smitten with love for her. So it was that she induced you to follow the wild ass, who was indeed the sorceress herself, that you might come upon the princess. She has had the name of the girl engraved upon the bezel of the ring—I know the man who made it. His name is Sa'd the engraver, and he lives in China.' Then the old man asked for wax, and, taking an impress of the bezel, he breathed upon the wax, when there appeared clearly the legend M H P R. At this, all that stood by were filled with amazement.

The prince then asked : ' Is the girl betrothed ? ' to which the old man replied : ' Not yet. I know of twenty-one princes who have wooed her, but they have never been able to fulfil the conditions she imposes.' Khurshidshah then asked : ' Why is that ? Does the king of China need much treasure, or is he a weakling that he countenances it ? ' The old man replied : ' The king has been brought to grievous sickness, from the fact that by magic the sorceress propounds various difficult tasks to the suitors, which must be carried out. One is the capture of a wild and savage horse, another is wrestling with an Abyssinian slave, and the third is to give the reply to a certain question so difficult that if any one can answer it the king will give him his daughter in marriage.

But whoever is unsuccessful is taken by the sorceress to her own apartment, there to be tortured.'

All were amazed that such things could be, but Khurshidshah burst out that he would lead a great army to China and win the princess at all costs. Upon hearing this the old man turned to the king and said : ' Let your son hearken to my advice and not do what he plans, for the wooing of the princess is beset with great peril, and his desire to see her is roused merely by his ignorance of her real state. To seek her can but lead to sorrow.' But the king replied : ' He is set now upon doing this.' He ordered that the old man should be given a robe of honour and a purse of gold ; and so dismissed him.

Now the king did not know that the old man was the sorceress, who had transformed herself for her own purposes. When the old man had departed the king turned to his son and urged him, now that he knew who the maiden was, to be consoled and strive to rid himself of his sickness. ' For ', said he, ' any object may be attained by health of body, and no wealth or empire in the world can be set against it for value.'

The prince took his father's counsel, and by careful regime was in a month restored to health. He rejoiced now in bodily strength, and going one day to his father, said : ' Your Majesty knows into what depths of sorrow I have been cast by love, and to what degree I have suffered bodily pain through excess of love. I crave now your permission to gird up my loins and go in search of the princess, for until I shall have found her I shall never find relief from melancholy.'

The king observed the eager tones of his son, but said : ' My son, remember the counsel of that old man, for it is only by following such counsel that one achieves one's desires. Beware also of putting upon your father too great grief. Remember that you saw the maiden only as she lay asleep. You know not her waking manners nor her way of life. You are still a youth, and have never before been parted from your father and your mother.'

The prince was smitten with grief at this reply, and weeping bitterly pleaded long and earnestly with his father. ' Father,' he cried, ' you cannot know the pain that is in my heart, else you would not thus increase my sorrow. You have never been afflicted by such bitterness of separation as I now suffer. When I saw the maiden, I loved her, not knowing who she was or whence she came. Now that I know, my love is increased a hundredfold. I pray you to let me depart ; if you do not, I shall destroy myself, for I have no more power to bear my anguish. It is not you that are plunged in the heart of the battle, you merely regard its progress, and to the spectator all warlike deeds are simple. If, on the other hand, you hesitate on account of the treasure or the army I must take with me, then let not that concern you, for I need neither the one nor the other. I will go alone, and by my own courage win her, or die. But whatever befall, let it be no source of grief to you.'

The king replied : ' Truly you know that it is no matter of treasure. You are my heir ; my treasures and kingdom must in the end come to you ; nor is it an army that grieves me ; but I am loath to drink the cup of sorrow that you force into my hand. But if you must go, let it be as you desire, and may your quest be prosperous ! ' The prince in great joy left his father, who thereupon commanded that the treasure houses be opened. From them he brought out great stores of jewels and gold and silver, musk and ambergris and camphor, robes of Rūm and Baghdad satin, to the extent of twenty ass loads : a tent also and a pavilion to dwell in, store-tents, a kitchen, water-carriers, and all else needful for a journey.

The king then summoned the two ministers Alyan and Alyar. To them he said : ' I desire you to accompany my son to China. He is yet young and does not know all the ways of the world, nor is he acquainted with the forms and ceremonies fitting to different occasions. The duty will fall upon you to enlighten him concerning what is proper.' The two ministers made obeisance, saying, ' We are slaves ; we will perform all that Your Majesty commands.'

Finally Marzubanshah appointed a thousand horsemen to escort the prince, and set Prince Farrukhruz over them. Then, the two ministers having made all ready, the prince bade his mother and sisters farewell and the caravan departed, amid the tears and wailing of the women-folk and to the sound of the beating of drums.

Stage by stage they journeyed, until at last the guide came to Khurshidshah and warned him that a desert of forty days' march was before them. ' We must have water, food and fodder in plenty, so that we may win across this desert.' Alyan and Alyar assured the prince that their food and fodder was sufficient for fifty days, and then, having filled all their water vessels, the caravan struck into the waste. It appeared to them as though no human being could ever have set foot there before. It was barren of water, not a blade of grass or a leaf was to be seen, the ground was flat and hot under foot, the dwelling place of divs and ghouls, most terrible.

They had crossed about a fifth of the desert when the demon of cupidity came upon Alyan and Alyar, and roused the evil that was in them. They took counsel together and said : ' Why should we submit to the commands of a youth ? Let us overwhelm him, seize all this great treasure, and ourselves become rulers and kings.' But the thought of what they must do with Farrukhruz troubled their minds. At last they decided that they must destroy both the princes, and then declare themselves supreme. ' The escort is with us,' they reasoned, ' and we can kill any man who will not make a compact with us.' They decided further that they would carry out their murderous design by means of poison.

One night, therefore, they summoned Timurtash, the slave of Khurshidshah, and, handing over to him a small packet containing poison, told him that when next the prince and Farrukhruz called for wine, he was to put this poison into the cup before he handed it to them. They promised that if he did this they would give him wealth beyond his dreams. Now the slave had a great affection for his master, and understood moreover that when he had carried out their treacherous plan he would in his turn become their victim. He therefore took the package, pretending to consent, but as soon as he could he went secretly to his master and warned him of what was afoot, at the same time showing him the poison.

The prince embraced him for his righteous deed, gave him a jewel-encrusted bracelet that he had upon his hand, and said : ' Contrive to give them this very poison. They would not have rewarded you had you carried out their design, but would have destroyed you. I will make you commander of my escort, my friend and confidant. I call Farrukhruz to witness also that my father shall be told of this, and he in his turn will reward you.'

When the caravan halted that night, and the ministers, as was their custom, came to the prince's tent to eat their meal and to drink wine, they made a sign secretly to the slave Timurtash, who by a glance reassured them. But he presented the poisoned cup first to Alyan and then to Alyar, and before he had time to take the cup from the latter's hand, both the traitors fell dead. The slave cried out : ' Thus may all your enemies perish, O prince. These traitors must be hung up, for no other fate befits them.'

The corpses were thereupon taken out and suspended aloft, while the prince announced to the whole camp what had occurred, and gave a robe of honour to Timurtash. He also appointed him to have charge of the treasures and made him his personal companion.

The next morning the caravan resumed its way. For days it marched forward until the desert had been left behind and inhabited country was reached once more. At the edge of the desert they came upon a city, where they rested for three days, and then continued their journey until one day there appeared in view the landscape of China.

Outside the gates of the capital they encamped, while from the walls a great concourse of people watched them. News was soon brought to the emperor that a strong company of armed men had encamped outside the gates, with many horses and much treasure. It happened that the emperor's vizier, Mihran, a man of world-wide experience, wise and understanding, was with him when the news was brought. Together they decided to send a chamberlain with a strong escort to find out who the new-comers were, whether they were friendly or hostile, strangers or neighbours, and what their business was.

Now while they sat encamped before the city gate, Farrukhruz, warned by the adventure in the desert, came to his brother secretly and said : ' If you trust my integrity and honour to represent you, it would be safer and better if you were to put on my robes and I yours, and that I pretended to be Khurshidshah and you Farrukhruz. When I am summoned to the emperor's court, I shall doubtless be asked that difficult question by the nurse-sorceress, and, failing to answer, shall be carried off. You will then remain, and will doubtless find some means of achieving your aim and of helping me. If not, then I will gladly die to help you.' After some delay Khurshidshah consented to this plan, and donned his brother's clothes. When, a few moments later, the emperor's messenger arrived, it was Farrukhruz that received him in state, while Khurshidshah waited in attendance, though none knew of the change. The ambassador made obeisance to Farrukhruz and greeted him in the name of the emperor, saying : ' The lord of the world, the emperor of China, commands me to ask what your race is, whence you come, what your desire is, and what reason brings you to this land,

so that we may carry out your wishes.' In reply
Farrukhruz said : ' Ambassador, carry my greeting
to the emperor, and say that I am Khurshidshah,
son of Marzubanshah, king of the country of
Halab, and of all the Syrias. It has been told me
that the emperor has a daughter, famed for her
beauty. My purpose in coming to this land was
to ask for the hand of the maiden in marriage.
I have no other concern. If he grant me permission, I will fly to put myself at his service and
kiss the ground at his feet ; if not, then I must
return disconsolate. Go to the emperor and make
my cause clear to him.'

The ambassador thereupon took his leave, and
on coming to the palace informed his master that
the stranger was a royal prince, who desired to be
his son-in-law. The king was thrown into the
greatest agitation by this news. Turning to his
vizier, Mihran, he said : ' What fate is this that will
make every monarch in the world my enemy, on
account of this daughter of mine ? Would she had
never been born, that I might escape these constant
troubles.' Mihran replied : ' From the world's
beginning it has been ever thus, that kings have
had daughters, and other kings have sought union
with them. Your trouble is not on that account—
for all kings suffer that—but on account of this
sorceress-nurse, who is a visitation from the gods,
and cannot therefore be overcome, unless per-
chance the gods grant their aid. For the moment,
however, it is necessary for you to receive the
youth, for he is a royal prince.'

The king gave orders that the town was to be
decorated, and a lodging prepared. Then, when all
was ready, he dispatched Mihran his vizier with

a number of courtiers and chamberlains and
a thousand horsemen, to the prince's camp.
Farrukhruz received them with great ceremonial,
and the vizier conveyed to him the king's message
that if he would so far incommode himself as to
proceed to the royal palace, his further pleasure
would be there awaited. The company then set
out. On their arrival in the city, they found it
splendid with adornment and resonant with music.
Passing through a lofty gateway carpeted with
Egyptian rugs and lined by rows of slaves in golden
headgear, they came after a series of curtained
passages to a mighty chamber four hundred paces
long and as many broad. It was splendid as Shah
Jamshid, paved with alabaster and turquoise,
having in the centre a great fountain, where gold
and silver fish swam in abundance. By this stood
a couch of ivory and teak, ebony and sandalwood,
and a great throne of gold and silver, upon which
sat the emperor himself. When the latter saw
Farrukhruz, he was charmed by his beauty, and
invited him to sit by his side upon the throne.
Then, while they feasted, the emperor spoke with
Farrukhruz, asking him why he came to this far
country. The prince repeated to him what he had
already said to the ambassador. Greatly moved,
the king replied : 'If I had a hundred thousand
daughters I would give them to your embrace, and
were you to ask for my kingdom I would give it
you. But, for the sake of your own welfare, do
not press me for my daughter. I know that it has
been spread abroad and is a matter of general
knowledge that I am helpless in the hands of
a sorceress-nurse, and that twenty-one princes
have been slain by her when they came to woo my

daughter. For your own sake and the sake of your father, whose heart I know must grieve at being separated from his son, I advise you to wait till the nurse has died, and then woo my daughter.' Without hesitation the prince assured him that far from waiting till the sorceress died, he could not restrain himself for a single day. For long they debated. At last the king summoned a courtier, by name Salih Lala, who was the princess's chamberlain, and sent him to her apartment with the message that a prince, Khurshidshah, had come from Halab to woo her. When the messenger came to the princess's door, the nurse was seated with her, and on hearing the king's message, she dressed the princess in her finery, and with her attendants led her into the king's presence. Needless to say how Khurshidshah gazed with all his strength at the maiden, love of whom possessed him. Farrukhruz, however, as courtesy demanded, kept his glance away from her and continued his converse with the king. When the nurse came before the king she called : ' Who is the suitor ? ' to which Farrukhruz replied : ' I am.' Then said she : ' Have you heard the legend, and seen the wild horse and the Abyssinian slave, and have you learnt the secret, and know who speaks of it ? ' He replied : ' If I had not acquainted myself with that matter, I should not have come.'

The next day the field of combat was made ready, and the king stood beneath a sunshade, while Khurshidshah in his own royal clothes came and stood in Farrukhruz's place, with Farrukhruz as his attendant. On his arrival the nurse gave orders that the horse be brought in, and, plunging madly, a piebald horse was dragged in by several elephants.

Khurshidshah sprang into the field, and the animal at once charged at him, head down. As it approached, the prince sprang aside and contrived to seize the animal by both ears, so that it stood helpless and quiet. He then saddled it and galloped backwards and forwards on the ground with the most marvellous horsemanship. A great cry arose from the beholders when they saw his skill, and again when he dismounted to receive the emperor's praise and a robe of honour in reward.

The prince and his brother spent the night with the king, and the next day at sunrise the company again went down to the open ground, which was thronged with spectators. Soon an Abyssinian slave came on to the ground, like a mountain for stature, and dressed in a pair of leathern drawers. There he stood, while Khurshidshah approached, like a cypress for beauty, so that all who looked on him were amazed. They sighed for him, and cursed the evil nurse. When the prince came to within a few paces of the negro, he uttered a great shout and flung himself upon him. The negro, too, launched himself like a demon upon the prince, so that both clung and swayed together. Then quickly disengaging himself the prince flung himself down to the ground, and seizing the negro by his two feet he raised him from the ground, lifted him over his head, and dashed him so violently to the earth that the negro's head, neck, and back were shattered. A roar from all the beholders signalled this feat, and Khurshidshah approached and kissed the king's hand, and the king in turn embraced him and clothed him in a robe of honour.

The nurse, thereupon, in high dudgeon bore off the princess to her own apartment, while the

populace departed homewards and turned the
night into bright day with rejoicing and feasting.
The emperor, having ordered the palace to be
decorated and illuminated, sent a message to
summon Khurshidshah to a feast. The prince
donned the garments of Farrukhruz and gave his
brother his own royal robes; then, on going with
him into the palace, he seated himself in his
brother's place. When they arrived they found
the accursed sorceress already present with the
princess. Almost as soon as the prince was seated
she turned to Farrukhruz, and said: ' Now tell
me what is the secret and who speaks of it, and
what is his description.' The king and Mihran,
his vizier, were dismayed at this speech, and
Farrukhruz, turning to her, said in wrath: ' This
is no riddle, but a stratagem. Were it a riddle
I might give you the answer to it now; but since
it is a stratagem I demand three days' respite
before I reply.' The sorceress refused to hear of
any delay, and leaping from her throne, seized
Farrukhruz and carried him off to her apartment,
while the princess followed in her footsteps. A
great cry and groans came from all the spectators
at this sight. The king, too, was utterly downcast.
Khurshidshah, full of grief, returned to his
lodging in the utmost misery. With his companions he sat down to mourn his brother, and
remained sorrowing for several days. One day,
when his period of mourning was ended, the prince
went to walk in the bazaar of the linen drapers, and
coming to the shop of Khwaja Sa'd the chief of the
drapers, who was his friend, entered it and sat
down. As they sat there conversing, a horseman
of remarkable bearing passed the door. After

him went a number of bold and warrior-like men
on foot, led by another man of notable and
courageous appearance. Turning to his friend,
the prince asked who this cavalier was, and who
the warriors that walked behind him and the man
that led them, for till that day he had beheld none
like them. Khwaja Sa'd replied : ' The horseman
is Shaghal Pilzur (the Jackal with elephant
strength), the chief of the nobles of the city, while
the warrior on foot, in the felt cloak and with
daggers at either hand, is the chief of the brigands.
He is known as Samak the Brigand, and is the
adopted son of Shaghal Pilzur. The others are
their companions, and between them they have
power over all the city, and form its army.' The
prince immediately thought to himself : ' If I need
help it is to him that I must go '; and so thinking,
departed to his lodging. There he dismissed
Timurtash, his constant companion, and advised
his attendants to scatter and let report of them be
as little heard as possible, lest they attract the
attention of the sorceress. Moreover, by their
doing so, he himself might carry out his plans with
less danger. Then, taking a purse of one thousand
gold pieces, he made his way to the house of
Shaghal Pilzur.

At the gate he found two sentinels, whom he
asked to announce the fact of his arrival to their
master. They replied : ' The gate of the chivalrous
is always open.' ' True,' he countered, ' but it is
not chivalrous or discreet to enter the house of the
chivalrous without permission.' Finally he was
admitted to the presence of Pilzur, who welcomed
him graciously as one of the defenders of Khurshidshah. After they had eaten together and drunk

wine, the prince turned to his host and asked:
'How many boundaries has chivalry?' He
replied: 'Chivalry goes beyond all boundaries,
but its greater sides are seventy and two, and out
of these, two are the choicest, one to provide bread
and the other to don armour. What now is your
need?' 'Since you describe the donning of
armour as of the essence of chivalry,' replied the
prince, 'I would ask your indulgence while I tell
you a secret that I have.' Pilzur swore an oath
that he would not repeat to any one what he was
told, and made his companions also swear.

'Then,' said the prince, 'you must know that
I am Khurshidshah, son of Marzubanshah, king
of Syria.' 'But, young man,' said Pilzur, 'I was
at the king's court when the nurse carried off
Khurshidshah before my very eyes. How can you
say that you are he? I desire nought but the
essence of truth.' 'That', said the prince in reply,
'was my brother Farrukhruz, who came with me
and shared the perils of the journey with me. It
was I that subdued the horse and the Abyssinian,
but on account of the riddle my brother gave up
his life for mine.'

When Pilzur realized the truth of this story he
said: 'The chivalry of Farrukhruz is greater than
any of ours,' and raising his cup he drank to the
hero's memory. Then he embraced Khurshidshah,
and said: 'We are sixty men, and we pledge
ourselves to the companionship and service of
Farrukhruz.' In the course of their conversation
the prince turned to his newly-found friend and
said: 'My brother, since your favour is so great,
I would ask if you can contrive in the morning
to let me see the princess, and so possibly gain

news of Farrukhruz from her.' He replied : ' My son, it is a difficult task that you demand. It cannot be achieved by a long purse, for that harem is surrounded by the fear of the sorceress. If it were an undertaking that might be carried out by gold, or strength, or by a stratagem, or by brigandage, then we might perform it, but none but a bird of mystery can fly round those walls.' Khurshidshah was greatly downcast, but suddenly Samak the brigand spoke, and said : ' Master, do not let the prince despair ; I have an inspiration, but cunning is needed. The princess has a companion, Ruh Afza, a woman full of charm and wit. I am her friend and she will perform all I ask. Through her it may be made possible for the prince and the princess to meet.'

In great joy they spent the day and part of the night in feasting. At cock-crow, Pilzur, Samak, and the prince arose and went together to the dwelling of Ruh Afza. Samak knocked at the door and was admitted by a slave-girl, who recognized him. As he entered, Ruh Afza, who had been asleep, rose from her couch and greeted him, asking why he came at that hour, and whether all was well. ' Yes,' replied the brigand, ' all is well, except that our chief, Shaghal Pilzur, and a friend are standing outside the door.' The woman hastily put on a robe and admitted them, gave them food and drink, and asked what their trouble was. Samak replied : ' Mother, you have often helped me, and once again I would desire you to hear me, and not let my words fall to the ground.' ' What is your need ? ' she asked, ' you know that if it be anything that demands secrecy I will never reveal it, and if you have anything to entrust you may

deliver it with confidence to me.' Samak thereupon pointed to the prince, and said : ' This youth,
whose name is Khurshidshah, is a king's son. He
has placed himself under our protection, and he has
come to this country to woo Mah Pari.' ' But ', she
cried out, ' is not Khurshidshah he whom the
sorceress carried off ? ' Samak then disclosed to
her the true state of affairs, and after further
colloquy urged her to devise some method of
attaining the prince's object.

After much thought she raised her head and
said : ' I have found a way, but what I say must
be obeyed in every letter.' Delivering the prince
into the care of Ruh Afza, Pilzur and Samak
then departed. The woman turned to the prince,
and impressed upon him once more the importance
of carrying out carefully all she said. Then she
dressed, adorned, and scented him like a woman,
told him his name would be Dil Afruz (i. e. the
Heart-Exciting), and set him amongst the slave
girls. Next day Pilzur and Samak came once more ;
bringing with them a casket containing a soporific
drug, and also a rope, both of which would, they
said, be of use to the prince. And so he remained
there for some time, practising the arts of a slave-
girl.

It befell some little time later that the feast of
the New Year was celebrated. Ruh Afza was in
attendance upon the princess, and walked with her
in the garden. The princess asked after her health,
whereupon her companion replied that she was well,
and had, as a New Year gift for her mistress, a
beautiful and accomplished slave-girl. ' Send for
her,' said the princess, ' and let me see her.' A
chamberlain was sent for Dil Afruz, and she came

in full beauty. Soon the princess asked her to sing and play, and this she did to the delight of all, so that the princess was greatly pleased with her, and, calling the girl to her side, gave her wine to drink and praised her.

At last, when the guests had departed, the princess said to Dil Afruz: 'You are skilled in all kinds of music, do you also play backgammon and chess?' 'A little,' was the reply. She gave an order to her slaves, and they brought chessmen made of fishes' teeth, hollowed and filled with musk and ambergris, and a playing board of leather stitched with silk, having sides of crystal. And so they played, and though the prince was more skilled, still he allowed his fair opponent's pieces to stand untaken.

The princess was delighted with the game. When it was over, she dismissed all her slave-girls and told her chamberlain to admit no one, for she desired to drink wine with her nurse and with Dil Afruz. Now it was the task of Dil Afruz to pour out the wine, and as soon as opportunity offered he put some of the soporific drug which he had brought with him into the goblets of the sorceress and the princess, so that both were soon unconscious. The prince was greatly tempted to slay the sorceress at once, but bethought him that she alone held the secret of his brother's fate. He carried her out of the apartment into the garden therefore, and tied her securely with his rope. Then, climbing the wall, he pulled her up after him, and let her down on the other side. Then he too leapt down, and putting her over his shoulder made for the house of his warrior friends. As he made his way in the black darkness, two men who

were coming towards him called out to him to halt,
and asked who he was. On coming nearer he saw
to his great joy that they were his friends Pilzur
and Samak, who had been warned by Ruh Afza
that their presence in the neighbourhood of the
palace-wall might be opportune that night. He
related what had occurred and handed over his
burden to them, then went back as he had come
into the palace.

The brigands carried the sorceress to their
castle. There they flung her down upon the floor,
so that the shock awoke her, and, to her great
anger and amazement, she found herself fast bound
and surrounded by bold-looking men. She
shrieked out on seeing them, asking who they were,
but their only reply was to demand the solution of
her secret, and to ask whither she had carried off
the prince. She refused any answer, though time
and again she was questioned, and at last basti-
nadoed heavily. But nothing could make her
speak, so that they left her impatiently in a
dungeon to await another opportunity.

Meantime Khurshidshah had made his way back
into the chamber where the princess lay. But he
could not sleep. The thought of his brother set
him roaming about the sleeping palace. By
chance he came to a vestibule, but as he entered,
a negro slave with a drawn sword in his hand
sprang forward, saying : ' No one may enter here.
This is the abode of the sorceress.' The prince
heard this with secret joy, but said : ' I am Dil
Afruz, the princess's minstrel maiden. I awoke
to find drink, for I was thirsty, but I have lost
my way.' Upon this the negro bowed low and
asked the maiden to enter and drink wine with him.

Khurshidshah eagerly agreed, and sat for some time pretending to drink, but plying the negro with wine until he fell into a drunken sleep.

Quickly, then, the prince arose, took up a lamp, and looked about him. In the course of his wandering he came into the courtyard of the castle to which the sorceress bore off her victims. In front of him was a door, upon which were nailed a number of human skulls. He tried it, and found it locked. Thinking to himself that the secret must lie behind that door, and that the key to fit it must be in the possession of the black slave, he returned, and to his joy found a key in the slave's pocket. The thought came strongly to him that Farrukhruz was alive and imprisoned behind the locked door. Quickly he unlocked it, and found before him a ladder stretching down into the darkness. Down this he clambered for more than fifty steps, finding himself at last in a large underground chamber in which were four doors, with a couch facing each. By the light of several candles which were burning, he saw a number of people bound hand and foot lying on the couches, and to his overwhelming joy in the midst of them he recognized Farrukhruz. To him he leapt and embraced him, while his brother asked him how he had come, and how it was that he had escaped the sorceress and the black slave. 'The story is too long to tell now:' replied the prince, 'look at my garb, and you will understand partly how I came.' As he spoke he untied the bonds that fettered his brother, who stood again upon his feet. 'And now,' said he to Khurshidshah, 'let us release these other princes, who have suffered like myself.' The prince replied that they must first swear an oath to reveal nothing of what

they had seen, and that they must remain in the
dungeon till the morrow, for the palace was strange
to him, and he did not yet know a favourable way
out. Also his disguise made it necessary for him
to be in attendance upon the princess. ' But,'
he added, ' be not afraid, I will send out and bring
men to help me, and by to-morrow you shall all
be free.'

So saying, he departed with Farrukhruz, locked
the door after him, and replaced the key in the
slave's pocket. Thence they made their way on
to the roof, where Khurshidshah tied his rope
round his brother's middle, and told him that when
he was outside the palace he must go to the quarter
of the straw-sellers, to the house of the cavaliers.
There he was to ask for Shaghal Pilzur and Samak,
and was to tell them all that had occurred. Also,
if any message was necessary, it was to be sent by
the hand of Ruh Afza. He then let his brother
down by the rope, returned to the princess's
chamber, and there slept until far into the morning.

Now Farrukhruz, as he had been instructed,
found his way to the castle of Pilzur and Samak,
and was admitted. To his amazement the sound
of the bastinado fell upon his ears as he entered,
but his wonder was soon allayed when he saw
that it was the old sorceress who was being
beaten. He presented himself to the chief brigands,
who greeted him warmly, and asked how he had
come and how he had left Khurshidshah. The
prince replied that all was well. As he spoke the
sorceress turned towards him, and seeing him she
cried out, ' How are you here ? Is my black slave
dead, and my palace destroyed ? ' Farrukhruz
tauntingly replied : ' You thought I was like the

others, a helpless youth come to woo the princess
to make sport for you, but I broke down your
palace and am free. To-morrow I will show you
all the other unfortunates whom you have tor-
mented.' Amid the curses of the wretched woman,
Pilzur and Samak departed with him to the house
of Ruh Afza. To her they told the story of what
had occurred, and asked her to bear to Kurshidshah
the message that they would station themselves
that night under the walls of the palace, and would
be ready to rescue him and the other princes.

Ruh Afza made her way to the palace and
found the princess feasting with her maidens. As
soon as occasion offered she whispered to Khurshidshah what plan had been made, and soon
afterwards took her leave. Night had fallen
before the feasting and the music were over. The
princess then dismissed all her slave-girls, and
Kurshidshah in his disguise made his way to
the black slave, whom he again beguiled with
wine and music till he lay in a drunken sleep.
Upon seeing the negro unconscious the prince
ascended to the roof, and from it saw his friends
with about fifty companions gathered below. At
once he let down his rope and pulled up Pilzur and
Samak, who ordered their men to wait. The three
friends then crept stealthily to the sorceress's
apartments, where they came upon the slave.
When the prince had taken the key of the dungeon
from his pocket, Samak destroyed entirely what
life remained in the negro. Together then they
climbed down into the dungeon, where they found
eight handsome youths bound hand and foot.
As he stood before them Samak told them that
the woman with him was Kurshidshah, who had

come to woo the princess and had faced enormous dangers in order to overcome the sorceress
and to reach the dungeon on their behalf. He
also made them swear an oath, that when they
were released they would no longer seek to win
Mah Pari, but would allow her to become the
wife of Khurshidshah. They were not to become
enemies of the prince on that account nor bear
him any grudge. His friends were to be their
friends and his enemies theirs. All swore the
oath that Samak desired, and he released them
from their bonds. But instead of ascending to the
roof they made their way to the gate of the palace,
and having overpowered the sentinels that stood
there, opened the gate and went out in safety;
Khurshidshah going with them.

When, next morning, the princess awoke and
called for her Dil Afruz she was greeted by the
answer that the slave-girl was not to be found.
The chamberlain whom she sent in search returned
with the answer that he could find no trace of her.
The princess at last went into the apartment of the
sorceress. To her amazement and horror she
found the negro slave, who had always guarded
the door, lying dead upon the ground, and as she
ventured farther, she saw that the door of the
dungeon was opened and the prisoners no longer
there. In great haste she ran to her father and
told him what had occurred, telling him in reply
to his questions, that for two or three days the
sorceress also had not been seen.

Now the king had just heard that the sentinels
at the gate had been overwhelmed and slain, and he
at once summoned his vizier. 'Some one', said he
to the minister when he arrived, 'has broken into

the nurse's dungeon, liberated the captives, and slain our sentinels. What can have become of the nurse ? My daughter has told me that for two or three days now she has not been seen.' The vizier replied : ' None but Pilzur and the brigands can have done this. Let someone be sent to inquire.' A messenger was immediately dispatched, who brought Pilzur and Samak to the palace. There they came into the presence of the king and the vizier. The latter in angry tones asked them how they had ventured to enter the very palace of the king, there to slay his sentinels and carry off the nurse. He told them also that only they could have done this thing. Samak, who was as skilled with his tongue as with his sword, then explained what had emboldened them to do what they had done ; how the prince Kurshidshah had implored their aid, and how he and his brother were now safely in their hands, as also were the other princes whom the sorceress had imprisoned. Also he declared that the sorceress herself was now in chains. ' If Your Majesty commands,' he concluded, ' I will bring them all into your presence.' ' Do so,' said the emperor ; and at once they departed. On their way back they brought with them all the princes, and sixty of their brigand comrades. As they passed through the city the rumour of what had occurred spread abroad, and at once a crowd of a hundred thousand people, men, women, and children, gathered round them and followed them, thronging the streets. Their way led through the gloomy bazaars, and as they passed there the thought came into the head of Samak, ' I will destroy this sorceress-nurse. She is neither a queen nor of noble birth, nor even the wife of the emperor,

that one is compelled to bring her to him. Nothing
will be better than that I should slay her, and free
the world from her.' Thinking thus, he drew his
knife and plunged it into the wretched woman's
bosom. So, with a great struggle, the sorceress gave
up the ghost and died.

The news of this went in advance of the company
to the king, who rejoiced greatly and received the
congratulations of all his nobles assembled there.

Now when Mah Pari heard the story she was
greatly disturbed at the thought that Dil Afruz
was in reality the Prince Khurshidshah, and that
he had penetrated into her apartments. Summoning her chamberlain she asked where the prince
was, and was told that he was in attendance on
her father. At once she went there, but could not
recognize him, until at last the emperor, saying
that he had heard of Khurshidshah's skill in
minstrelsy, invited him to sing. When the prince,
after some hesitation, did so, Mah Pari was so
greatly pleased with his appearance that she fell
deeply in love with him.

Now it happened that Mihran, the king's vizier,
had a son who also desired Mah Pari for his wife.
He had long loved her in secret, but had been
restrained by fear of the sorceress from venturing
to woo her. Now that the sorceress was dead,
though he saw that Khurshidshah was so greatly
in favour, he went to his father and begged him
to help in winning the princess. In the midst of
Khurshidshah's playing, therefore, while all were
intent upon the singer, the vizier spoke to the king
in the following fashion: ' It is not hidden from
Your Majesty, that the wickedness of the dead
sorceress-nurse gained for you the enmity of many

kings, whose sons, having come to woo your
daughter, were imprisoned and slain by her. Also
your subjects suffered much at her hands, and are
ready on small provocation to revolt against you.
It would soothe both the foreign monarchs and the
populace if a further test could be devised, whereby
all the princes now in China might compete against
one another for the hand of the princess. Thereby
would be obviated all jealousy of Khurshidshah
amongst the suitors, and your subjects, in the
pleasure of the spectacle, would forget their past
sufferings.' ' But ', the king objected, ' Khurshidshah has shown his worth and his valour before all
men.' ' True,' replied the cunning vizier, ' but if
you deliver the maiden to Khurshidshah without
some plausible excuse, these princes will go each
to his own country and return with armies
to destroy you. Let them do battle one with
another, in single combat, on the parade ground,
and let your daughter be given to the victor. Thus
will the mouth of the whole world be closed, and
none will feel himself injured by you.'

The king at last reluctantly consented, and was
telling Mihran to devise a plan for the contest when
Samak the brigand, who had been standing near,
and had overheard the conversation, came forward
and said to the emperor : ' Your Majesty, the
maiden is now Khurshidshah's. He has won her
by his courage and skill, and no man has a right
to cast his glance upon her. For whom does
Mihran desire your daughter, that he speaks thus ? '
Mihran replied : ' The populace must be pacified,
and only the spectacle will calm them.' And so
the matter was arranged and announced to all
present. The vizier's son was filled with glee at

the plan, and boasted to those around him : ' If an
elephant were to come against me I would take
it up and rend it.'

That evening the emperor was filled with
anxiety concerning Khurshidshah, for he desired
him greatly to be his son-in-law, and Mah Pari also
loved him. Summoning her chamberlain, she gave
him a royal robe, the price of which Allah alone
knows, and a black horse, the choicest in the king's
stables, together with a saddle and bridle with
trappings of gold and jewels. She bade him take
these to Khurshidshah in secret, that people might
not see.

She herself next morning sought her father's
permission, and went, concealed from the eyes of
men, to the battle-ground. Soon Khurshidshah,
dressed in his royal robe and riding upon the black
charger, came on to the field, followed by Farrukhruz, Samak, and Pilzur, and their sixty men-
at-arms. Before the king he halted and did
obeisance, and the king replied graciously.

The princess's suitors were all present upon the
field. Going to the king they told him that they
had no quarrel with Khurshidshah, and indeed had
sworn an oath when he rescued them from the
sorceress, that they would leave the princess to
him and bear no grudge. At the vizier's request,
however, the king released them from the oath and
the contest was opened.

The first that rode out was the vizier's son,
Bahman, the brother of Mah Pari's suitor. In loud
tones he sent out a challenge to any of Khurshidshah's following, and a knight rode forth towards
him. At once the youth engaged him and thrust
his spear so cleanly at him that it pierced through

his back. Again and again the youth made his challenge, till at last twenty men lay dead on the field. Khurshidshah then arose to do him battle, and, seeing him arise, Mihran called out: ' Consider well ! do you not see how he has trampled on all his opponents ! ' But Khurshidshah called out : ' As you, by setting down one letter after another, become at last skilled in writing, so I, by seeing his errors, know by what trick to overcome him.' Setting his horse into a gallop against Bahman he avoided his thrust, but as he passed he seized him by his waist-belt and lifted him from his horse high over his head. Then he flung him down violently to the ground. As he turned, he saw waiting another son of the vizier, he that sought Mah Pari's hand in marriage. Then at last he knew what the vizier intended, and cried out to the vizier : ' If you had a hundred sons, I would overcome them all.'

Samak, who was watching, warned Kurshidshah to make no mistake, for his opponent was a warrior of skill and experience. But the prince, going boldly towards his rival, drew a great sharp-edged dagger from his bosom, and when he came near leaped upon him and plunged the dagger into his breast. When the vizier beheld this, by a signal he summoned a great crowd of men on to the battle-ground in the hope of doing Khurshidshah an injury, but the brigand chief and his men forced a guard round the prince and together they returned to their castle.

The next day the prince went to the royal palace to arrange for his wedding. At first the emperor wished it delayed for forty days, but on Kurshid-shah's pleading with him he agreed that the wedding should be celebrated within ten days. Content with this the prince spent the following days in preparation. But on the seventh day, Samak, who had been inquiring secretly in the town, told Pilzur and the prince that the vizier was greatly enraged at the slaying of his two sons, and might attempt to carry off the princess, or to do her an injury. That night, therefore, by means of a rope he climbed into the palace, and entering the chamber where the princess lay sleeping, with all care wakened her and told her who he was and why he had come. Gladly the princess agreed to go with him to Khurshidshah, and together they went on to the roof, and the brigand, tying his rope about her waist, let her gently down to the ground. Then he himself followed and brought the maiden to her lover, who bore her off to his own country. There he lived for long with her in all happiness and luxury.

[MS. Ouseley 379.]

GLOSSARY

Dīnār.	A gold coin, mostly worth about ten shillings.
Dirham.	A small silver coin (Greek drachm).
Dīv.	Evil genius ; demon.
Frang.	Europe.
Ghoul.	A demon inhabiting lonely places. It may have one of many shapes and colours and devours men and animals.
Hammām.	Public baths (hot).
Hind.	India.
Jamshīd.	Jam the Brilliant, the most famous of the legendary kings of Persia.
Kāfir.	Unbeliever.
Khatīb.	Reader of prayers in the mosque ; preacher.
Maund.	A weight of about two pounds.
Peri.	Good genius ; fairy (male or female).
Qalandār.	A member of an itinerant order of ascetics.
Qāzī.	Judge ; generally the administrator of ecclesiastical law, but he could also try civil and criminal cases.
Rūm.	Byzantium.
Salām.	' Peace ! ' (greeting).
Sheikh.	A devotee, learned in religion and the holy law.